ENVIRONMENTAL SCIENCE, ENGINEERING AND TECHNOLOGY

G000016285

THEORY AND APPLICATION FOR WARNING AND PREDICTION OF DISASTROUS WEATHER DOWNSTREAM FROM THE TIBETAN PLATEAU

ENVIRONMENTAL SCIENCE, ENGINEERING AND TECHNOLOGY

Additional books in this series can be found on Nova's website
under the Series tab.

Additional E-books in this series can be found on Nova's website
under the E-book tab.

CLIMATE CHANGE AND ITS CAUSES, EFFECTS AND PREDICTION

Additional books in this series can be found on Nova's website
under the Series tab.

Additional E-books in this series can be found on Nova's website
under the E-book tab.

ENVIRONMENTAL SCIENCE, ENGINEERING AND TECHNOLOGY

THEORY AND APPLICATION FOR WARNING AND PREDICTION OF DISASTROUS WEATHER DOWNSTREAM FROM THE TIBETAN PLATEAU

XIANGDE XU,
XIAOHUI SHI
AND
CHUNGU LU
EDITORS

Nova Science Publishers, Inc.

New York

Copyright © 2012 by Nova Science Publishers, Inc.

For permission to use material from this book please contact us:
Telephone 631-231-7269; Fax 631-231-8175
Web Site: http://www.novapublishers.com

NOTICE TO THE READER

Library of Congress Cataloging-in-Publication Data
Xu, Xiangde.
 Theory and application for warning and prediction of disastrous weather downstream from the Tibetan Plateau / Xiangde Xu, Xiaohui Shi, and Chungu Lu.
   p. cm.
 Includes bibliographical references and index.
 ISBN 978-1-62100-433-2 (soft cover)
 1. Flood forecasting--Tibet, Plateau of. 2. Flood warning systems--Tibet, Plateau of. 3. Tibet, Plateau of--Climate. I. Shi, Xiaohui, 1972- II. Lu, Chungu, 1958- III. Title.
 GB1399.2.X83 2011
 551.6551'5--dc23
                          2011051308

Published by Nova Science Publishers, Inc. † New York

CONTENTS

PREFACE

One of the most conspicuous features of the Earth's surface is its dramatic rise of land on the north side of the Southeast Asia, known as the Tibetan Plateau. Two facts substantiate this breathtaking landmark. One is the height that it arises above the sea level. The average elevation of the Tibetan Plateau is over 4000 m. Many of these lands sit almost at the middle of the "sky" (troposphere). The second is the vast land-areas that it covers. The Tibetan Plateau accounts for nearly 1/4 of the total land area of China, is about four times of the size of France. Although the human population inhabiting this vast land is not large, there is about 40% of total world population living in the periphery of this highland, including the two most populated countries and fastest growing economies in the world: China and India.

Because of its unique topographic features, the Tibetan Plateau plays an important and special role in the global atmospheric energy and hydrological cycles. It stores huge amount of water resources due to accumulation of snows and glaciers over an immense geological time scale. It also produces the world densest natural hydrological systems, such as rivers, streams, and lakes. The Tibetan Plateau is also the reason why the world largest monsoon system exists, which brings indispensible rainfall in the surrounding regions. Yet the monsoonal precipitation can be a source of a huge grief for people living in the area. It causes a flood when it rains too much; while it becomes a drought when it rains too little. The atmosphere can also be disturbed by the rise of the land. The intensification of the disturbed airflows can grow into severe weather systems, which can cause disastrous conditions downstreams. These problems are extremely important to the countries on the downwind side of the Tibetan Plateau, mainly Eastern China, Japan, and Korea.

In 1979, China carried out the first scientific expedition on the Tibetan Plateau to investigate its role in the global atmospheric circulation. In 1998, Chinese and Japanese scientists had jointly conducted the second atmospheric science experiment over the plateau. One of the important results obtained from these studies is an understanding of the plateau's "atmospheric pumping" dynamic mechanism. The Tibetan Plateau acts as an atmospheric pump which attracts warm and moist air from both Indian and western Pacific Oceans. This atmospheric energy and water vapor transport and convergence are further complicated and intensified by the effect of Asian summer monsoonal circulation.

On the basis of many results from the previous studies, several key scientific questions are put forward: Whether the particular atmospheric boundary-layer (ABL) and orographic features of the Tibetan Plateau can form a particular type of atmospheric heat source? How does land-ocean-atmosphere interaction characterize the associated water circulation processes? Are these energy and water circulation features important controlling factors for the East Asia and China's disaster weather and global climate change? How convective clouds over the plateau affect the occurrence of East Asian river floods and droughts? To answer these questions, the authors have conducted a series of theoretical, modeling, and observational studies. As a result of these studies, a New Integrated Observational System over the Tibetan Plateau (NIOST), supported by China-Japan joint international cooperation project (JICA), has been implemented since 2005 and in operation since 2009. The NIOST provides an unprecedented platform for studying land-atmosphere interaction, weather and climate related to the Tibetan Plateau and its global impacts.

This book includes authors' research results in a recent decade or so, which tries to unravel the secret of water and energy cycle systems on the plateau and the impact of these systems on weather and climate. We also want to assess the ability of the developed observing network in the Tibetan Plateau in providing crucial meteorological information, which can be used for monitoring, prediction and early warning of disaster environmental conditions.

Our works were supported jointly by the Chinese National Natural Science Foundation as a key project (No. 41130960), the International Science and Technology Cooperative Projects funded by Ministry of Science and Technology of China (2009DFB20540), the social commonwealth research program of Ministry of Science and Technology of the People's Republic of China(GYHY201006009), the China-Japan intergovernmental cooperation program supported by Japan International Cooperation Agency (JICA) -

"China-Japan Meteorological Disaster Cooperative Research Center", and the Independent Research Project of LASW (2009LASWZF02, 2008LASWZI04).

Chapter 1

THE DOWNSTREAM IMPACT OF THE TIBETAN PLATEAU CONVECTIVE CLOUDS AS PERTURBATION SOURCES

The Tibetan Plateau is the largest and highest plateau in the world. Because of its unique geographic feature, the Tibetan Plateau plays important roles in global weather and climate systems. In particular, due to its elevated land surface and strong radiative heating, the Tibetan Plateau becomes a favorable place for initiating a large number of convective cells. These convective cells over the plateau are often evolved into severe storms downstream, carrying typical characteristics of "lee cyclone." Furthermore, the plateau acts as a large-scale air pump, attracting warm-moist air from Indian Ocean and South China Sea. The water vapor will converge on the southeast side of the Tibetan Plateau, and then turn to the east. The abnormality of the downstream transport of water vapor often results in flooding and/or drought conditions in many East Asian countries. Finally, as a gigantic heat source, the plateau also takes an exclusive role in the Indian and East Asian summer monsoon, which brings about the largest monsoon rainfall on Earth.

Since 1979, China and other collaborative countries, such as Japan and United States, have jointly carried out several field experiments to investigate the role of the Tibetan Plateau in the global atmospheric circulation and the impact on the downstream development of disastrous weather systems. One of the important results obtained from these previous studies is an understanding of the "atmospheric pumping" effect caused by the plateau topographic features. The Tibetan Plateau attracts warm and moist air from both the Indian and western Pacific Oceans. This atmospheric energy and water vapor transport and convergence are further complicated and intensified by the effect of the East Asian monsoon circulation (Figure 1). The eastern branch of the water vapor flux starts from east of the Philippines, moves into the South China Sea, and then turns toward East China. The western branch extends all the way back from East Africa near Somalia, then moves through the Arabian Sea, the Indian Ocean, and over the Tibetan Plateau via the Bay of Bengal, then turns to the east. The two branches converge on the east side of the Tibetan Plateau, and then continue to move down to the Yangtze River basin in China and into other East Asian countries, including Japan, Korea, etc. (Xu et al. 2008a).

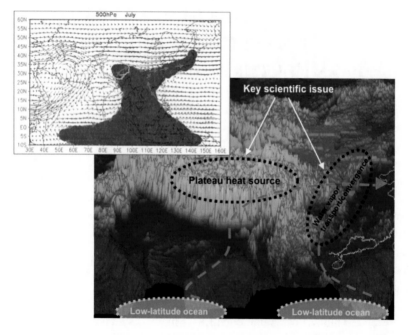

Figure 1. Schematic plot of orographic features of the Tibetan Plateau, its surrounding areas, and the adjacent oceans (color background). Blue arrow curves indicate the typical paths for moist transport from low-latitude oceans to East China and Japan. These paths are based on 1958–95 summertime mean water-vapor flux calculated from NCAR/NCEP reanalysis data, shown in the upper-left panel graph (highlighted with red arrows that indicate predominant water-vapor fluxes with effective northward transport). The yellow contour encompasses the area with an average land-surface elevation above 4,000 m.

Because it is the largest and highest plateau in the world, the Tibetan Plateau plays an important role in the global atmospheric energy and water cycles. The large water resource stored in this region and its downstream transports support nearly 40% of the world population, including China, India, and many Southeast and East Asian countries (Xu et al. 2008b). The Tibetan Plateau accounts for nearly one-quarter of the total land area of China, but meteorological and other environmental observational and operational stations are scarce over this vast land. This has contributed to the uncertainties in the prediction and warning of high-impact weather over the plateau and regions downstream, and in the monitoring and diagnostics of global climate (Xu et al. 2008a).

In view of the crucial role of the Tibetan Plateau in global energy and water circulations, several international organizations, such as the World Meteorological Organization (WMO) and United Nations' Environmental Program (UNEP) have advocated several initiatives about an international cooperative effort on integrated global observing systems for climate and environment, especially strengthening the observations over the world's key and sensitive regions, such as the Tibetan Plateau. In particular, the WMO's World Weather Research Program (WWRP) has issued a collaborative plan, called THORPEX (THe Observing System Research and Predictability Experiment). One of the ideas in this plan is to stress that a high-impact weather system usually has its corresponding sensitive area in its upstream region, and the observations over this sensitive area are most effective in improving the forecasting and warning of high impact weather (THORPEX-China 2005).

The southeastern edge of the Tibetan Plateau is just located on the path of moisture transportation from the Bay of Bengal, South China Sea, and tropical western Pacific to the Yangtze-Huaihe Rivers basin (Zhang 1999; Hu and Ding 2003). All these components form a "large triangle" of land-ocean-atmosphere interaction (Figure 1). As a heat source/sink, the Tibetan Plateau poses large impacts on the weather and climate over its downstream areas, i.e., the Yangtze-Huaihe Rivers basin and the regions of south China and East and Southeast Asia (Ye and Gu1955; Ye and Gao 1979; Ye 1981; Chen et al. 1985; Ji et al. 1986; Yanai et al. 1992; Yanai and Li 1994; Zhao et al. 2001; Wu and Zhang 1998; Xu et al. 2002; Xu et al. 2008a, b).

1.1. STRUCTURAL CHARACTERISTICS OF CLOUDS ON THE PLATEAU

The first scientific experiment over the Tibetan Plateau was conducted in 1979. One of the findings obtained in this field campaign is that the characteristics of the plateau temperature and humidity fields as well as the general circulation patterns are quite favorable for convective plume to develop on the plateau. Flohn (1968) estimated the occurrence frequency of cumulonimbus (Cb) by means of satellite cloud images, and pointed out that the Cb clouds on the southeastern Tibetan Plateau could be described as a "chimney effect" of atmospheric heat transfer. Statistic results from Dai (1990) showed that the annual mean occurrence frequency of Cb on the plateau is 2.5 times as many as that in other areas of China, close to that in the southeast coastal areas of China, where the occurrence frequency of Cb is high due to abundance of water vapor. The boundary layer observations from the field experiments showed a strong atmospheric inverse radiation over the Tibetan Plateau, which indicated that water vapor may also be abundant locally in the atmosphere. The surface turbulence was distinct and the thermal mixed layer was deep in the boundary layer over the plateau. All these results suggested that the plateau surface possessed suitable conditions for the formation of mesoscale cumulus convections. The radar observations during the Tibetan Plateau Experiment (TIPEX) in 1997 also discovered that the convective clouds presented as column cells with small horizontal scale and deep vertical height over the plateau. From a set of satellite images for an extraordinary torrential rain process in the Yangtze River area from June to July of 1998 (Wang and Yang 2000), we can characterize these convective clouds into a "pop-corn-like" cloud system (Figure 8). As shown in Figure 3, these convective clouds (marked by small "a"s) occurred and developed on the middle and eastern parts of the plateau and moved eastward during the development of a flooding process along the Yangtze River. These pop-corn-like convective cells eventually formed into mesoscale cumulus convective systems (marked by the big "A"). Figure 3(a) shows the initiation period of developing process of a "pop-corn-like" mesoscale convective system at 06:00, UTC 20 July 1998 over the middle part of the plateau, Figure 3(b) illustrates its developing and organizing stage at 08:00UTC, Figure 3(c) shows the strong development of mesoscale cumulus convective system and the formation of matured mesoscale system at 10:00UTC, and Figure 3(d) shows the formation of a matured mesoscale cloud cluster over the plateau and its transport eastward at 12:00UTC 20 July 1998.

Figure2. Columnar dust whirl at Garze, Tibet.

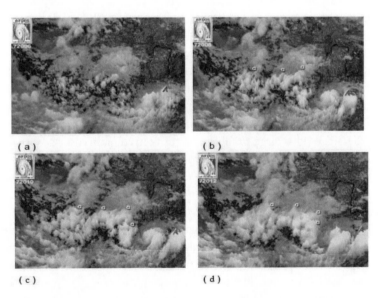

Figure 3. The four development stages of a plateau mesoscale convective system viewed from the satellite: (a) Initial formation stage, (b) development and organization stage, (c) mature stage, and (d) eastward movement and out of the plateau. The times for (a), (b), (c), and (d) are 0600, 0800, 1000, and 1800UTC 19 July 1998, respectively.

In the downstream regions, this mesoscale convective system became a major precipitation generator, and caused a severe flood in the Yangtze River basin in 1998.

1.2. THE CHARACTERISTICS OF DISTRIBUTION AND EVOLUTION OF PLATEAU CONVECTIVE SYSTEMS

Ye et al. (1979) analyzed the geographic distribution and daily and monthly variations of convective clouds on the Tibetan Plateau. They found that the most convective clouds were located in the central and eastern portion of the plateau, and some were also in the southeast of the Tibet and northeast of India. Zhu and Chen (2006) suggested that the region with most frequent convective sctivities in Asia was centered at (30°N, 90°E), with three main active regions: the Bay of Bangle-India, the Tibetan Plateau, and South China Peninsula. There were two major convective sub-regions over the Tibetan Plateau. One was located in south-central plateau, and the other was on the southeast side of the plateau, centered about (29°N, 100°E). In addition, the convective activities displayed yearly, monthly, and daily variabilities.

In the summer of 1998, a series of extraordinarily torrential rains occurred in the Yangtze River basin. Analyses from satellite data indicate that the cause of this heavy rainfall was a series of weather systems characterized with cyclonic and shear winds. These low-pressure cyclones could be traced all the way back to the convective activities occurred on the Tibetan Plateau. The plateau, with its geographic push, strong radiative heating, and availability of moisture, triggered a large numbers of convective embryos. As shown in the previous section (e.g., Figure 3), these convective thermals further developed into "pop-corn-like" cloud clusters. As these mesoscale convective systems moved eastward and progressed down slope, they gained more vorticity, and possessed a "lee cyclone" signature.

To track these eastward propagating convective systems, we analyzed cloud-top temperature from satellite data, which provides a good measure of convective activities (Maddox 1980). Figure 4 shows a meridional-time evolution of 3-hourly cloud-top temperature from Chinese satellite measurements for the heavy precipitation episodes during the 1998 China flooding events. It is seen from these pictures that the convective clouds originated over the Tibetan Plateau (90°-95°E), and they propagated eastward to the Yangtze River basin in eastern China (110°-120°E). As these convective systems moved out of the plateau, they further intensified.

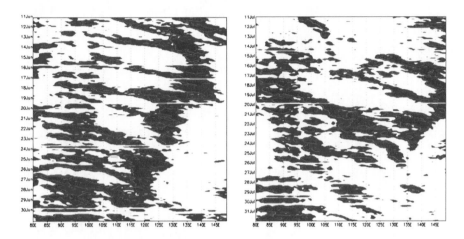

Figure 4. Meridional-time evolution of cloud-top temperature from Chinese weather satellite measurement during a) 11-30 June, and b) 11-31 July 2008 flooding events in the Yangtze River basin.

Chapter 2

AN UNDERSTANDING OF LAND-AIR DYNAMICS AND THERMAL STRUCTURE ON THE TIBETAN PLATEAU

The Tibetan Plateau occupies a quarter of Chinese total area, with its mean elevation about 4000 m. The plateau has the largest area, highest elevation, and the most complex topography in its kind in the world. The vast area of abnormal thermodynamic and dynamic structures due to land-air physical process on the plateau will obviously produces profound effects on global climate variation and disaster weather formation in eastern and southern parts of China, eastern Asia, and even the whole world. The areas are mainly wildernesses and deserts with low population. Meteorological observations are sparse with relative short historical data on the plateau. Therefore, it is not surprising that the understanding of meteorological variation over the plateau and its effect on disaster weather and climate are very limited (Zhang and Zhu 1988; Yasunari 1980; Hahn 1975). In order to reveal the characteristics of the plateau land-air interaction, over the past three decades, Chinese scientists organized two major field experiments on the plateau. These experiments also brought attentions from international community, and made cooperation with scientists from Japan, United States, and South Korea.

2.1. FIELD EXPERIMENTS ON THE TIBETAN PLATEAU ATMOSPHERIC SCIENCE

The first Tibetan Plateau Meteorological Experiment (QXPMEX) was conducted in the period from May to August 1979 (Ye and Gao 1979; Zhang and Zhu 1988). It is the first time that a large volume of scientific data of intensive observations and research results were obtained on the Tibetan Plateau meteorology and its effect on climate. The second Tibetan Plateau Experiment of atmospheric science (TIPEX) was conducted in the period from May to August 1998 (Tao et al. 2002; Yasunari et al. 2000). Scientists from China, Japan and other countries participated in the cooperative projects in the plateau experiment. The key objective of the projects was to perform the scientific experiment on the plateau atmospheric boundary layer. The advanced observation technique was used in the scientific experiment.

The base stations for the boundary-layer observation were built for TIPEX in four locations over the plateau. They are stations in Garze, Damxung, Qamdu, and Nagqu. In addition, there were many branch stations (Figure 5).

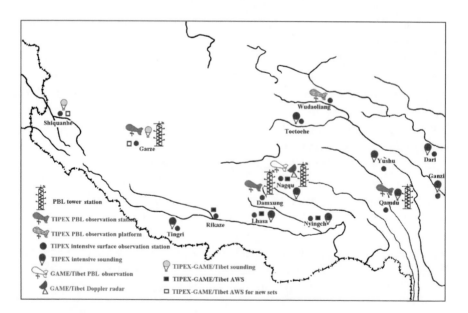

Figure 5. Distribution of stations for boundary layer observations, radiosonde, and surface intensive observations during TIPEX in 1998.

More than ten organizations took part in the boundary-layer scientific experiment, such as the Chinese Academy of Meteorological Sciences, the Institute of Atmospheric Physics of Chinese Academy of Sciences, the National Center for Marine Environmental Forecasts, Peking University, etc. The project provided various advanced instruments and equipments for the experiment, such as wind-profiler, gradient tower with 6-7 observational level (20m), Bowen ratio system, sonic anemometer-thermometer that measures temperature and humidity fluctuations, infra-radiation thermometer, Doppler acoustic radar, tethered-balloon, radiosonde with high resolution, optical rain gauge, radiation meters for probing short wave and long wave, direct and scattered radiation. TIPEX obtained valuable data for atmospheric boundary layer at the stations mentioned above. In addition, radiosonde, radiation and conventional observations during the intensive observational period (IOP) were conducted (Zhou et al. 2000). The distribution of observation stations was described in Figure 5.

2.2. PLATEAU ATMOSPHERIC RADIATIVE INVERSION AND DISTRIBUTION OF WATER VAPOR

The atmospheric radiative inversion is related to air temperature and water vapor content. In the clear-air condition, the atmospheric radiative inversion is mainly caused by long-wave radiation transmitted by water vapor in the atmosphere. At Garze, Qamdu, and Damxung the atmospheric radiative inversion exhibited a small daily variation in dry and wet periods. The daily maximum values of atmospheric inverse radiation in dry and wet periods are 331 W/m^2 and 351 W/m^2 (at Garze), 352 and 362 W/m^2 (at Damxung), and 339 W/m^2 and 361 W/m^2 (at Qamdu), and the daily minimum values are 285 W/m^2 and 309 W/m^2 (at Garze), 256 W/m^2 and 307 W/ m^2 (at Damxung), and 263 W/m^2 and 305 W/m^2 (at Qamdu), respectively. It is clear that the maximum and minimum values of atmospheric inverse radiation for these three stations in the wet period are larger than those in the dry period, indicating that in the wet period, the atmospheric inverse radiation increases with increasing water vapor content in the atmosphere. The values of water vapor content in the middle and east parts of the plateau are larger than those in the western plateau. Note that Damxung is located in an area with a large atmospheric inverse radiation and rich vapor content in the plateau. This water vapor state provides the middle part of the plateau with an important environmental condition to produce convective cloud clusters.

2.3. THERMODYNAMIC STRUCTURE OF SURFACE LAYER ON THE PLATEAU

The Tibetan Plateau may be treated as a heat source intruding into the free atmosphere through the transfer of radiative, sensible, and latent heat from the plateau surface and boundary layer. Ye et al. (1979), Nitta (1983), and Luo (1987) in their studies demonstrated that in the Northern Hemisphere, the summer maximum heat source is located over the Tibetan Plateau. Flohn (1968) considered that the heating effect of the Tibetan Plateau penetrating into the middle troposphere is an important mechanism for causing and maintaining of Asian summer monsoon.

The soil heat flux in most of the observational stations did not exceed 4% of the atmospheric heating (absorbed radiation) from the surface during the QXPMEX on the plateau. The proportion of soil heat flux to absorbed radiation has obvious time-space differences, reaching on an average above 7% in the western part of the plateau, and around 4% in the middle and eastern parts of the plateau.

There were many observational evidences showing that the instantaneous total radiation flux on the Tibetan Plateau and other areas is larger than the solar constant (Lu and Zhou 1995), and the similar phenomenon appeared many times in the period of TIPEX. In the summer of 1992, the peak record for the instantaneous total radiation on Mount Qomolangma was 1688 W/m^2, about 23% larger than the solar constant. The observations during TIPEX also showed that the total radiation is larger than the solar constant in many different areas of the plateau. Although the onset of rainy season in the Qamdu area is earlier than that in Damxung and Garze, the phenomenon that the instantaneous total radiation is higher than the solar constant was observed in all the months from May to August. In general, this phenomenon appears around noon when a great deal of cumulus appears in the sky, but the sun is not covered by clouds. From the serial records of radiation observations, we found that 17 out of 40 observational days at Garze show that the total radiation is larger than the solar constant, with the maximum value of total radiation reaches 1655 W/m^2, about 21% larger than the solar constant. In the record for a sampling period of 30 days, the case with the total radiation exceeding the solar constant was recorded for 32 times (mostly during noontime). At Qamdu the total radiation exceeding the solar constant appeared for 28 days within 84 observational days, the maximum total radiation was 1530 W/m^2, about 12% larger than the solar constant. In the records of radiation observation for 35 days at Damxung there were only two days for the 10-min average total radiation exceeding the solar constant, the maximum value was 1394 W/m^2, about 2% larger than the solar constant, but the instantaneous radiation exceeded the solar constant many times. Previous research showed that the so-called total radiation exceeding the solar constant is limited to the meaning of instantaneous maximum in general, but the TIPEX observational results showed that by means of a 10-min average value, the records of total radiation exceeding the solar constant were also observed at Garze and Damxung.

The mean total radiation from May to August of 1998 at Ali and Garze reached 340 W/m^2, with the maximum value above 370 W/m^2, which is higher than the maximum value of 352 W/m^2 observed during QXPMEX. The total radiation value on the Tibetan Plateau is the largest in the world. It is much higher than the maximum value (320 W/m^2) in the tropical regions and subtropical desert areas in Northern Hemisphere. The characteristics of strong radiation on the Tibetan Plateau could result in dynamic effects due to its obvious heating forcing and cause strong thermal convections on the plateau. The average daily variations of surface heat source intensity (Q_D-Q_G) in dry and wet periods at Garze, Damxung, and Qamdu have a simple daily variation characteristic. The peak appears before and after noon, and the minimum value appears before sunrise. It is mainly determined by the daily variation of total radiation. The heating intensity in wet period is larger than that in dry period. The largest heating intensity was recorded at Damxung, with its peak values in dry and wet periods 567 and 606 W/m^2, respectively.

At Garze, the peak values in dry and wet periods are 313 and 422 W/m^2, respectively. The smallest is at Qamdu, with the peak values of 321 and 389 W/m^2, respectively for in dry and wet periods. The ratio of sensible heat to heating intensity in dry period is 76% at Garze, while in wet period the sensible heat and latent heat have the equal proportion, and each occupies around 45%. In the dry period the sensible heat is the main factor in heat source strength at Damxung and Qamdu, with the ratios being 79% and 77% respectively, while in wet period the latent heat is the main factor, with the ratios being 58% and 69%, respectively. The heat balance components, i.e., the net radiation Rn, sensible heat Qh, and latent heat Qe in Damxung (in the middle of the plateau) are larger than those in Garze and Qamdu, suggesting that the surface heating intensity in the middle of the plateau is larger than that in the western and eastern parts of the plateau. The distribution condition of surface heat source as described above may be related to the regional characteristics of strong convective systems in the middle of the plateau.

2.4. CHARACTERISTICS OF PRECIPITATION PROCESS AND SNOW COVER ON THE PLATEAU

The observational results of Garze, Damxung, and Qamdu show that the onset date of rainy season has been pushed back while the rainfall intensity has been increased from west to east. The precipitation data of 1979 and 1998 at Lhasa and Nagqu have shown that the onset of rainy season in 1998 was later than that in 1979, but during the IOP the total amount of daily maximum precipitation in 1998 is equivalent to that in 1979 (indicating larger precipitation intensity). The characteristics in the water cycle on the plateau may affect the evolution of the East Asian monsoon in China. The difference of water vapor channel in the west or south edge of the plateau in different years may contribute to the annual variation of monsoon surge process in the East Asia.

Snow cover poses another important factor for the general circulation variations over the plateau, which is also an important part of the climate system. The snow cover in large area and its inhomogeneous distribution on the plateau could change the thermodynamic structure of the plateau's underlying surface. Figure 6a and b are the climatologically mean snow cover distribution and the snow cover distribution obtained from the satellite SSM/I data in January 1998, respectively. It can be seen from Figure 6 that the area of snow cover on the middle plateau in January of 1998 is obviously larger than the climate mean situation. From the distribution characteristics of snow cover in winter and spring of 1998, we found that the snow cover anomaly on the plateau in that period, especially in the middle plateau as shown in Figure 6, are characterized by decreasing in the south and increasing in the north. The snow cover anomaly on the plateau's underlying surface could induce the anomaly of land-air physical process over a large area in winter and spring. It would also exert an influence on the East Asian mean circulation pattern. This kind of thermodynamic structure in winter and spring on the plateau could be one of the most important influencing factors on general circulation and also an important relevant factor for precipitation and summer drought-flood conditions in the downstream regions.

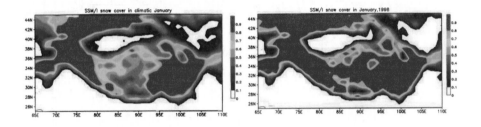

Figure 6. SSM/I plateau snow cover area distribution in January: a) climatological average; b) 1998.

2.5. THE CHARACTERISTIC OF THERMAL CONVECTIVE PLUME AND ITS VERTICAL MOVEMENT ON THE PLATEAU

Dynamically, in the convective boundary layer the buoyancy is the main forcing mechanism to drive turbulence, and this kind of turbulence is not completely irregular and can be organized into a thermal bubble or plume with distinguished structures (Young, 1988a, b, c). As for the Tibetan Plateau with its average height 4000 m, thus small air density and abnormal buoyancy, the turbulent characteristic in the boundary layer over the plateau is considerably different from that over the plain. The analysis of observational data by acoustic radar at Damxung for the period of planned IOPs indicated a characteristic of narrow-column convective plume in the boundary layer. The vertical speed at the center of the plume reached 1 m/s. On its sides appeared the symmetric subsidence areas (see Figure 7). The time scale of convective plume calculated based on the acoustic radar detection data at Damxung is 1.2-1.5 h, indicating that mesoscale convective motions are very active in the middle of the plateau, such as the dust whirl at Garze (Figure 2). The strong convective activities observed in the lower layers of the atmosphere in the period of TIPEX show that the frequent occurrence of cumulus over the plateau is related to the special dynamic structure of turbulence and convection in the plateau boundary layer.

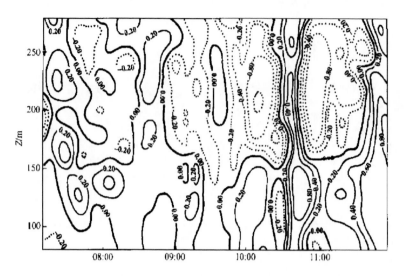

Figure 7. Time-height section of vertical speed detected by acoustic radar at the
Damxung Station during 0800-1200UTC 20 May 1998.

Through the above analyses, a comprehensive physical pattern of land-air
process in the surface and boundary layers on the plateau may be drawn as
follows:

1) The strong development of mesoscale convection and small-scale
    turbulence on the plateau is related to the local strong total radiation.
    Thermal inhomogeneity of the underlying surface on the plateau
    results from the strong heating source and complex topography of the
    plateau and the interaction of warm-wet and dry-cold advection in the
    lower atmosphere at the lateral boundary of the plateau. Therefore, a
    strong instability is typically generated at low levels on the plateau.
    The strong inverse radiation and humidity inversion in the middle part
    of the plateau, which are related to the distribution characteristics of
    water vapor advection from the lateral boundary mentioned above,
    create a favorable condition for developing mesoscale convection on
    the plateau.

2) The thermal plumes detected by acoustic radar often occur in the
    lower layers of the atmosphere on the plateau. They appear as a well-
    organized mesoscale and small-scale turbulent motion. The time scale
    for the occurrence of plume is 1.2-1.5 h.

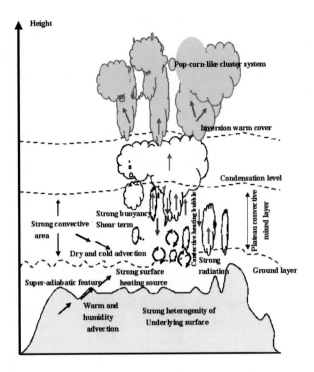

Figure 8. Physical description of boundary layer dynamic, thermodynamic, and turbulent processes in the development of "pop-corn-like" clouds and convective cloud clusters on the Tibetan Plateau.

3) The contribution of buoyancy and shear effects in convective activities in the lower layers of the atmosphere is larger on the plateau than on the plain areas. The convective activities on the plateau are an important mechanism for the formation of local and lateral boundary energy convergence and water vapor transfer.

4) The analysis of data from the IOP radio-sounding with high vertical resolution shows that there exists a deep thermal mixed layer on the plateau. In this layer the mesoscale and small-scale turbulent structures can develop or merge into large thermal convective cells. Some convective cells can further merge into a convective cloud cluster, in which a completely convective mixture typically occurs. A deep convective mixed layer was typically observed. Its depth is close to the thickness of dynamic boundary layer calculated by the wind vector analysis. The vertical variation of wind vectors appears in the form of Ekman spiral, indicating that there are strong turbulent

motions in the friction layer. There also exists an effect of the thermal convective activities related to the strong turbulent buoyancy, shear terms and deep thermal convective mixed layer, which could form a unique dynamic and thermodynamic triggering mechanism for the development of convective clouds.

5) The convective clouds are formed frequently on the plateau. Under the strong turbulence mixing and anomalous ascending motions, strong convective plumes and deep convective mixed layers on the plateau were observed. They could break through the capping inversion layer and form the frequently observed "pop-corn-like" cloud structure on the plateau. This cloud system could develop further to form a deep and matured super convection cloud cluster, and then move eastward. These observations support that the Tibetan Plateau area might be one of the most important sources of convective cloud systems generating heavy precipitation in eastern China.

The above dynamic and thermodynamic structure, as well as the characteristics of turbulence and convective clouds in the plateau surface and boundary layer provides a comprehensive physical picture (Figure 8), which reveals the boundary layer dynamic and thermodynamic structure and the mechanism and key influence factors for the occurrence of convective clouds on the plateau.

Chapter 3

SEASONAL MARCH
OF THE LARGE-SCALE
TOPOGRAPHY OF CHINA
TO THE MEIYU RAINBAND

The most pronounced spring-summer precipitation over the East Asian countries is related to the "Meiyu" (in Chinese, meaning "plum rain"), "Baiu" in Japanese, and "Changma" in Korean. The term "Meiyu" originates from the fact that the arrival of this rainy season coincides with the season when plums ripen in southern China ("Mei" means plums; "yu" means rains in Chinese). During the Meiyu season, large-scale precipitation covers most of Eastern China, the Korean peninsula, and Japan as it forms a large rainband across the Japanese Sea (Figure9). From the figure, one can see that with the seasonal transition from spring to summer, a large amount of water vapor is transported from the Bay of Bangle into China to support the Meiyu rainfall. This large-scale rainband presents a distinctive slow northwestward movement throughout the summer season. The northward expansion of rainfall seems to relate to the intensification of a subtropical high located at the southeast coast of China, in the western Pacific. Many previous studies also indicated that the position and intensity of western Pacific subtropical high controls the movement of Meiyu rainband (Ninomiya and Muraki 1986; Kato 1989; Tao et al. 2001; Ren et al. 2004). However, fundamental questions remain: why and how does the subtropical high intensify? Is there a fundamental physical process that dictates all these? There are several other large-scale influential factors that are important to the development of Meiyu rainfall, such as the southwesterly moisture transport, South Asian high, and Tibetan Plateau orographic effects (Murakami and Huang 1984; Xu et al. 2004; Qian et al. 2004; Zhu et al. 2007).

This chapter reports on a unique study of the Meiyu rainband and its movement, taking advantage of observational data from a dense network of meteorological stations over China (Figure 10). The surface data are provided by National Meteorological Information Center under the China Meteorological Administration (CMA). These surface data include precipitation, surface temperature, and surface-air (at 1.5 m) temperature (SAT) observed in 740 weather stations from 1957 to 2007. For upper air data, we used U.S. National Center for Environmental Prediction (NCEP) and National Center for Atmospheric Research (NCAR) reanalysis dataset.

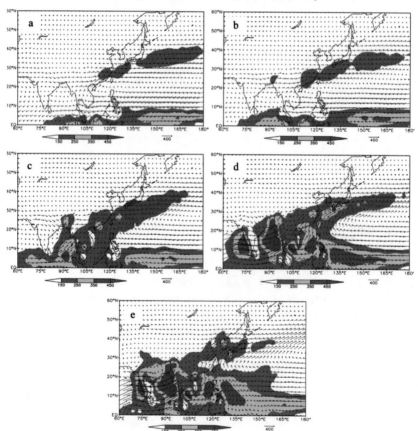

Figure 9. Averaged (1957-2007) monthly precipitation (color-shaded, in unit: mm) and column water vapor flux (arrows, in unit: kg m^{-1} s^{-1}) for the East Asia region (panel a - e are for March - July, respectively).

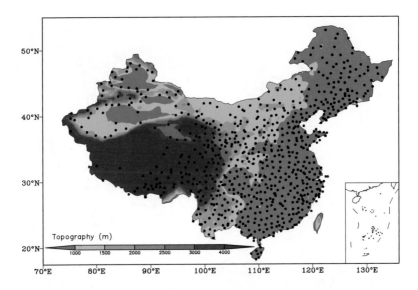

Figure 10. Distribution of surface meteorological observational stations in China used in this study. The background colors indicate land surface topography.

These data will be analyzed to gain some physical understanding, and then used to compute correlation and statistical verification of the analysis results. We will concentrate on precipitation patterns over eastern China in relation to large-scale topography of China.

3.1. THE MARCH OF THE MEIYU RAINBANDS

The Meiyu front is a part of the Asian summer monsoon, which is characterized by a seasonal wind reversal due to a land-ocean thermal contrast and the elevated Tibetan Plateau. The Asian summer monsoon is regionally divided into the East Asian summer monsoon and the South Asian summer monsoon (Indian monsoon) (Tao and Chen 1985; Ding 1994; Ding and Chan 2005). Because of the Tibetan Plateau's distinctive geographic feature (the highest and largest plateau in the world) and location, it serves a key role in both East Asian and Indian summer monsoons. The role of topography of the Tibetan Plateau in the Asian monsoon and regional water and energy cycle has been widely studied (Ye and Gao 1979; Ding 1992; Yanai et al. 1992; Lu et al. 2005; Xu et al. 2008).

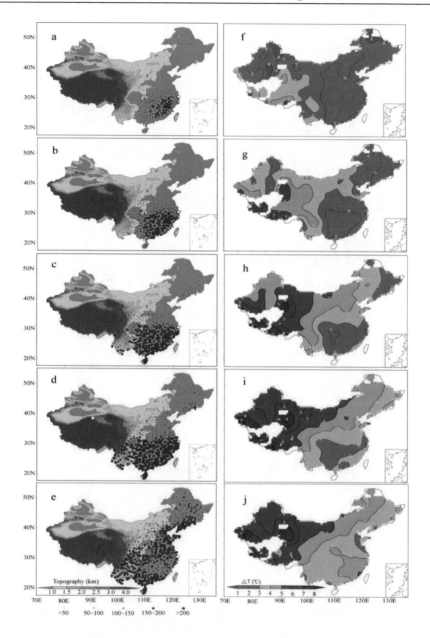

Figure 11. Left panels: averaged (1957-2007) monthly total precipitation in China. The amount is plotted as the size of blue dots, and the color-shades indicate the elevation of topography. Panels a)-e) are for March-July. Right panels: averaged (1957-2007) earth surface and near-surface air temperature difference (color-shaded, and the white areas are data void regions). Panels f)-j) are for March-July, respectively.

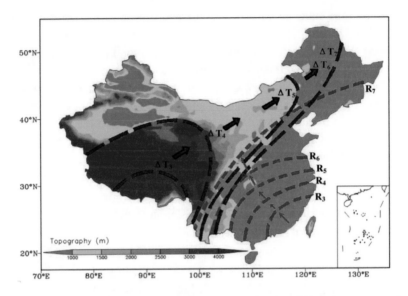

Figure 12. China's topographic distribution (color-shaded), monthly movements of Meiyu rainbands (red curves), and monthly movements of land-atmosphere temperature difference (blue curves). $R_3, R_4, \ldots\ldots R_7$ denote boundaries of 150-200 mm total monthly rainfall amount, and $\Delta T_3, \Delta T_4, \ldots\ldots \Delta T_7$ denote boundaries of land thermal forcing, respectively, from March, April, to July.

The dynamical effect of the Tibetan Plateau could have an influence on the Asian summer monsoon with an "air pump" effect (Wu and Zhang 1998). Several modeling studies (e.g., Zhu 1990; Zhu and Hu 1993; Wu and Ni 1997) indicated that if the Tibetan Plateau were absent, monsoonal rainbands would be trapped in the subtropical regions. The topographic reality of the Tibetan Plateau is responsible for the existence of monsoonal rains over much of the eastern Asian countries. In a review paper by Wu (2004), the author pointed out that the surface sensible heating due to the Tibetan Plateau plays an important role in the East Asian atmospheric circulation. Using thirty numerical experiments under different land-sea distributions and Tibetan Plateau topography conditions, Zhang et al. (2006) concluded that the elevation of the Tibetan Plateau is a key factor for the transition of the paleo-environmental pattern from "planetary-wave-dominant type" to "monsoon-dominant type."

One of the most striking features related to the East Asian summer monsoon is the marching of the Meiyu rainband over the East Asian countries, particularly over China. The Meiyu rainband is defined as the most northwest boundary of the spring-summer rain area in China (Tao and Chen 1985). The monsoonal rain starts in early March of every year in the southeast part of China (Figure 11a). Then it develops and expands in area to the north and northwest (Figs. 11a-e; larger blue dots indicated total monthly rainfall in the range of 150-200 mm). In July, the rain usually covers most of eastern China, to the north as far as Northeast China, but, remarkably, the Meiyu front stops, relatively abruptly and uniformly, along the general topographic line in western China. In August (not shown), the rain begins to retreat and decrease as autumn and winter set in. If one traces the Meiyu rainbands (rigorously defined as the boundary where the averaged monthly precipitation amount reaches 150-200 mm), a clear marching front can be found from March to July, denoting as R_3 to R_7 (red dashed curves in Figure 12). The rainband marches to the northwest as spring and summer evolve. In consideration of seasonal development of Meiyu rainfall, only monthly mean fields are discussed here.

3.2. INTERACTION OF THE MEIYU RAINFALL AND CHINA'S LARGE-SCALE TOPOGRAPHY

Many scientists have studied the Meiyu rainband in relation to the East Asian summer monsoon (Tao et al. 1958; Zhang and Tao 1998; Xu et al. 2004; Ge et al. 2008). All of these research findings point to the role of the Tibetan Plateau in the formation of Meiyu precipitation. For example, the early on-set of Meiyu in the southeast coast of China, as shown in Figs. 11(a) and (b), is related to a prompt thermal response of the Tibetan Plateau to the solar radiation due to seasonal transition from winter to early spring. However, the facts that the Meiyu rainband propagates to the northwest and stops along a line that coincides with the general topographic distribution of China indicate that there are more players in this land-ocean-atmospheric interaction, than just the Tibetan Plateau. One obvious suggestion for this is that western China's topography is aligned in a southwest-northeast orientation, clearly visible in Figs 11 and 12. Along this line, the topography jumps in three big steps: from the Tibetan Plateau (averaging over 3000 m in the red-shaded area) to the Loess Plateau (averaging over 1000 m in the yellow-shaded area) and down to the sea level (in the green-shaded area). Does this cascade of land elevation towards the northeast have anything to do with the northwestward propagation of the Meiyu fronts?

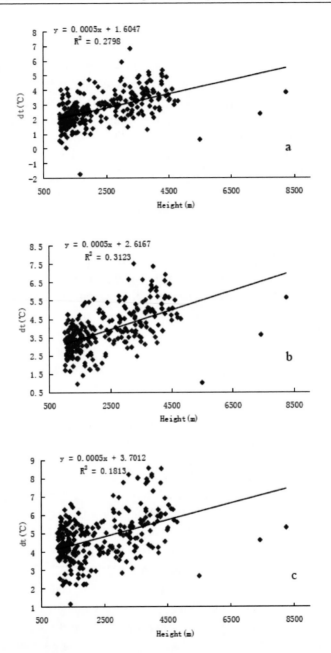

Figure 13. Correlation between elevation and land-surface air temperature difference for observational sites > 1000 m. (a) March; (b) April; and (c) May.

The answer is almost certainly positive if one understands how monsoonal precipitation occurs over many parts of the world where topographic features interact with surrounding oceans during a monsoon season. When the spring-summer season starts, a large landmass warms up relatively quickly, while the adjacent oceans tend to have a slow response to this seasonal change due to larger specific heat of ocean water. As a result, continents become relatively warmer places than oceans, and surface winds begin to converge over the land, which trigger convection, and rain starts. The monsoon circulation not only causes wind to converge over land areas, but also brings in abundant water vapor from low-latitude oceans (Xu et al. 2003). A higher elevated land with a larger landmass tends to receive more radiative heating and hence drives a stronger monsoonal circulation than a lower and smaller land. Therefore, the thermal driving force for a monsoon circulation is related to the size and altitude of the land, and reflects the seasonal change of exchange of energy between the sun and the Earth's surface. Scientists use sensible heat flux, F, to measure this radiative energy exchange, which is expressed as

$$F = \alpha \rho c_p (T_s - T_a)|V|$$

where α is a drag coefficient, ρ is air density, c_p is air specific heat at constant pressure, T_s and T_a are earth surface and near-surface air temperature respectively, and V is wind speed. A larger sensible heat flux represents a larger warming of the Earth's surface, and thus a stronger thermal forcing that drives a monsoon circulation. Notice that this quantity is proportional to the degree of the temperature difference between Earth's surface and near-surface air. In this study, both Earth's surface and near-surface air temperature can be obtained from 740 surface observations (Figure 10). The Earth surface temperature is the same as soil skin temperature, while the near-surface air temperature is the shelter temperature measured at about 1.5m above the ground. Therefore, it is reasonable to use $\Delta T = T_s - T_a$ to depict a thermal forcing for various land surfaces. We computed correlation coefficients between ΔT and land elevation for various months. The results indicate that the temperature difference between Earth's surface and near-surface air is positively correlated with land elevation (see Figure 13) throughout the development period of monsoon (from March to May). That is, the higher the land surface, the larger the temperature difference, and thus the stronger the thermal forcing. Therefore, with the transition from spring to summer, the cascade of western China's highlands will result in a spatial-temporal variation of land-air temperature difference.

In Figs. 11f-j, we have plotted the temperature difference between the Earth's surface and near-surface air for March, April, May, June, and July averaged over a 50-year period (1957-2007) (the data and measurements used in this calculation is described in Figure 10). One can see that in early spring (March and April), a signal of stronger ΔT first began to occur over the Tibetan Plateau. Then this signal propagated to the north and northeast. This development is consistent with China's major topographic feature, which jumps from the Tibetan Plateau to the Loess Plateau to sea level in Northeast China. In response to this increased land-atmosphere temperature difference, the Meiyu rainband marched towards the northwest. This interaction between the development of land-surface thermal property and the movement of the Meiyu front is summarized in Figure 12, where we denoted land thermal forcing as ΔT_3, ΔT_4,......ΔT_7 from March to July, and marked monthly development of this thermal forcing in blue curves. The analysis indicates that the intraseasonal development of Meiyu precipitation is closely related to China's large-scale geographic feature. The cascade of western China's elevated lands towards the northeast seems to act as a "dynamic attractor" that leads the Meiyu rainband to move towards northwest. The Meiyu rainfall propagates from southeast coasts of China towards northwest inland in a radiative fashion, and eventually forms a southwest-northeast rain belt. This is so because the thermal effect forced by the topography of western China tends to attract convection, resulting in rainfall that moves more and more inland towards the west. As rainfall moves westward, the thermal forcing expands towards the northeast. Therefore, the Meiyu rainbands gain a northward component of motion, in addition to their westward component. As a result, as the thermal sources forced by topography expand northeastwards, the Meiyu rainbands move towards northwest in response.

We also calculated month-to-month land-surface air temperature differences in the plateau region at meteorological stations above 1000m elevation and monthly total precipitation amount in eastern China (east of $100^\circ E$). The monthly distribution of ΔT and R is plotted on Figure 14a. It can be seen that the two fields show a very similar seasonal variation, except that the precipitation in eastern China lowlands tends to reach a peak in July, while the land-air temperature difference in western China highland tends to peak one month earlier.

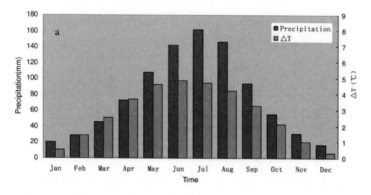

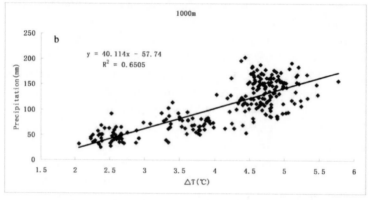

Figure 14. a) Monthly distributions of averaged (1957-2006) land-atmosphere temperature difference (ΔT) for stations above 1000m in western China (blue bars) and total precipitation amount (R) for stations east of 100°E. b) Scatter plot of March-July ΔT and R.

In order to reveal the forcing mechanism of land cascade on the development of Meiyu, we calculated a time-lagged correlation (one month) between land-air temperature difference for stations over the plateau (> 1000-m altitude) and total precipitation in eastern China (> 100°E longitude). The scatter plot is shown in Figure 14b. One can see that these two variables present significant correlation. This lagged correlation also implies that the land-air temperature difference over western China's highlands lead, in time, the development of Meiyu rainfall in estern China' lowlands, and thus suggesting that the north and northwestward movement of Meiyu rainband may be forced by the large-scale topography in China. The drop of the land elevation from the Tibetan Plateau to the Loess Plateau to Northeast China lowland results in a secession of increase of land-air temperature difference towards north and northeast over these regions, which may provide a precursor for north and northwest extension of Meiyu rainfall in eastern China.

3.3. THE INFLUENCE OF LARGE-SCALE TOPOGRAPHY ON THE STOP OF MEIYU FRONTS

Finally, we want to explain why the Meiyu front stops along the edge of elevated terrain over western China. The averaged flow pattern in the west-east cross section is shown in Figure 15. The westerly downslope wind (with a sinking motion component) is clearly shown along the eastern slope of the topography below 805hPa (between 105-120°E). The stronger downslope wind is located near the foot of the plateau, and it gets weaker as blowing further east. In early spring, land-surface thermal forcing is relatively weak and confined to the Tibetan Plateau region, and the monsoonal flow (blowing from ocean to land) on the southeast side of China is relatively weak. Therefore, the downslope westerlies and monsoonal flows most likely meet in the southern portion of China not far from the oceans (the convection and rainbands are confined to the areas marked by R_3 and R_4 shown in Figure 11 and 12). As the land thermal forcing intensifies (ΔT increases both in intensity and in area towards northeast), convection produced by the convergence of westerly and monsoonal flow occurs farther inland and extends further north and northwestwards. Depending on the strength of the monsoonal flow, it can overcome some of these weak downslope winds and is still able to get the rain going. However, as it approaches the plateau, the convection becomes harder because of stronger downslope wind. Finally, when the land-surface thermal forcing is fully developed in July, the Meiyu rainband moves to the foot of the elevated land, where convection is suppressed by downslope winds. These places mark the terminus of Meiyu front motion.

To further demonstrate the point, in Figure 16 we also plotted a horizontal distribution of one-month time-lagged correlation between the land-air temperature difference on the plateau and the whole-column water vapor fluxes (vector field; from surface to 300-hPa level), composite with surface precipitation (color-shaded). As we can see from this figure, the correlated moisture fluxes come strongly from low-latitude oceans and western Pacific into China. These fluxes gradually weaken as they approach to the western China's highlands.

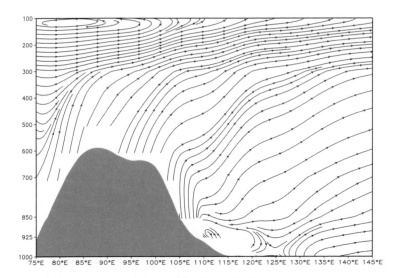

Figure 15. Vertical cross-sections for atmospheric circulations (denoted as streamlines) in the west-east vertical plane along 30°N.

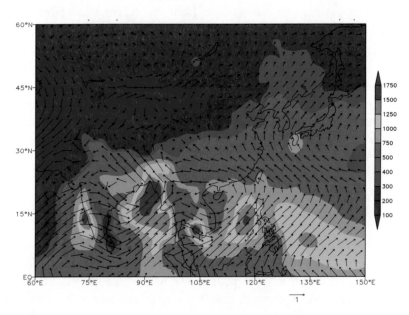

Figure 16. horizontal distribution of one-month time-lagged correlation between land-air temperature difference on the plateau (> 1000m altitude) and the whole-column water vapor fluxes (vector field), composite with surface precipitation (color-shaded) in East Asia area.

The movement of these correlated water vapor fluxes is very similar to the Meiyu rainfall expansion shown in Figure 3, i.e., the water vapor fluxes propagates north and northwestward in a radiative fashion from the southeast coasts of China. As the fluxes decrease along the line of western China topography, the associated rainfall also diminishes. Eventually, the moisture fluxes loose the strength, and rain stops along the topographic line (Figure 16).

3.4. SUMMARY

In summary of this chapter, we have uncovered a mechanism for the development of the Meiyu rainfall in China based on the calculations using a half-century of wind, Earth's surface and near-surface air temperature, and precipitation data. We found that with the seasonal transition from spring to summer, the cascade of land elevation from the Tibetan Plateau to Loess Plateau to lowland in Northeast China induces a spatial-temporal variation of land-air temperature difference, which contributes to an enhanced sensible heating of land surface. Such a sensible heating in turn intensifies the summer monsoon driving force due to a land-ocean thermal contrast. In particular, the successive development of sensible heating following the cascade of China's large-scale topography possesses a time-lead correlation with the north and northwestward movement of the Meiyu rainband. The large-scale topographic thermal forcing is intrinsically liked to the variation of subtropical high over the western Pacific. The Meiyu rainband stops right along the boundary of western China's highlands, where the downslope westerly winds tend to suppress convection. It is also shown that the topography of the plateau blocks landward transport of water vapor, which provides another cause for Meiyu rainfall to stop along the topographic line. This phenomenon also explains the distinctive dry-wet contrast between China's highland and lowland regions.

Chapter 4

THE WORLD WATER TOWER AND WATER VAPOR "RE-CHANNEL" EFFECT BY THE TIBETAN PLATEAU

4.1. THE WORLD WATER TOWER EFFECT OF THE TIBETAN PLATEAU

The Tibetan Plateau has always been referred to as the "roof of the world." Covering about a quarter of China's total land area, the average elevation of this land is over 4000 m. This elevated land plays an important role in global natural and climate environment, and results in the most pronounced monsoon circulation on Earth. The Tibetan Plateau is also a natural museum for mid- and low-latitude glaciers, snowpacks, frozen land, and plateau vegetation. Thousands of lakes and glaciers are scattered across this vast region. The area of lakes and the snow/ice storage in this region account, respectively, for 52% and 80% of total lake area and glaciers of entire China. The water resource from these lakes, glaciers, and rivers over the plateau and its immediate downstream regions (including Yunnan, Guanxi, Sichuang, and Qinghai provinces) accounts for about 47% of total surface water resources in China (Tung 2002; Ding 2002). These highland waters are carried down to the surrounding regions via a large network of streams and groundwater aquifers. It is here that many of China and Asia's major rivers originate, such as the Yangtze, Yellow, Indus, Mekong, and Ganges Rivers, comprising the largest river runoff from any single location in the world (Ding 2002; Lu et al. 2005). These waters have been sustaining life, agricultural, and industrial water usage for nearly 40% of the world's population, including

China and India, the two emerging economical powers (UNEP, 2007). The upper-level atmospheric moisture transport also affects the entire global natural and climate environment. Combining all these facts, it is not an overstatement to call the Tibetan Plateau "the global water tower." It is vital to understand the atmospheric roles in maintaining of these waters over the Tibetan Plateau, the atmospheric circulations and transports of water vapor to this part of the world, and the trend of the water vapor supply during recent global warming.

4.1.1. The Characteristics of Water Vapor over the Plateau

To maintain this water tower transporting water to the surrounding areas, there must be a sustainable supply. Obviously, the melting of glaciers and atmospheric precipitation are the continuous supply for the ceaseless water runoff. While a lot of mountain glaciers and snowpacks have been accumulated through an epic time scale accompanied by a dynamic evolution of the formation of the plateau, the atmospheric precipitation has been the ultimate supply to this water storage (Lu et al. 2005; Davis et al. 2005; Duan et al. 2006). Furthermore, for annual river discharge over the Tibetan Plateau, precipitation contributes the major amount for the outflow waters. Lu et al. (2005) showed that glacial meltwater constitutes about 7.2% of total river discharge from the Tibetan Plateau in China. The questions are then what the characterization of the atmosphere water vapor over the Tibetan Plateau is, where this water vapor comes from, and what a special role the plateau's geographic feature plays in this ocean-land-atmospheric interaction. Figure 17a shows a horizontal distribution of 59-year averaged annual mean water vapor content (black contours) between a 500-300 hPa atmospheric layer (the red dashed line marks the Tibetan Plateau). The data used in this calculation is from the U.S. National Center for Atmospheric Research and the National Centers for Environmental Prediction's 59-year reanalysis (1948-2006). One can see from this calculation that the atmosphere presents a distinctive pool of water vapor maximum right above the Tibetan Plateau. Further calculation of a 59-year mean moisture distribution for summer in the vertical cross sections along a meridional direction (Figure 17b: averaged for $80°E - 110°E$) and along a latitudinal direction (Figure 17c: averaged for $27.5°N - 35°N$) shows that the elevated lands (including the Tibetan Plateau and North American Rockies, shaded in dark brown) effectively push moisture up. Due to its significant rise-up in altitude and extensive coverage spatially, the Tibetan Plateau seems to exert an effect of atmospheric water characteristics on a global scale.

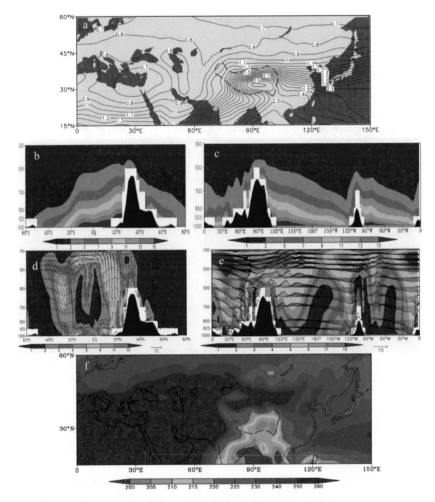

Figure 17. Horizontal distribution of 59-year (1948-2006) averaged (a) annual mean column water vapor content (contour, in kg m^{-2}) between a 500-300 hPa atmospheric layer; (b) vertical cross sectional distribution of mean summer specific humidity (in unit: gkg^{-1}) in the meridional direction (averaged for 80°E-110°E); (c) same as (b), except in the latitudinal direction (averaged for 27.5°N-35°N); (d) wind vector and speed (color-shaded, in unit: ms^{-1}) in the meridional vertical cross section (averaged for 80°E-110°E); (e) same as (d), except in the latitudinal vertical cross section (averaged for 27.5°N-35°N); and (f) averaged summer OLR (color shaded, in Kelvin) during 1975-2006. Dark brown-shaded in (b)-(e) are topography.

On its east side, the moisture slopes down all the way across the Pacific and to the foot of the North American Rockies. On its south side, the moisture slopes up from Southern Hemispheric oceans, crosses the Equator and into the Northern Hemisphere, and climbs up the Tibetan Plateau. These results provide a more complete picture of the Tibetan water tower: in the atmosphere above, a pool of concentrated water vapor serves in the role of "water-supply tank"; at the surface, glaciers, snowpacks, and lakes serve as a "water-storage pool"; and all the rivers connecting to the plateau function as "water pipelines" that transport water away. The upper atmosphere channels in and out moisture, which affect the entire world's water environment. We verified this result using a half-century's (1957-2006) upper-air radiosonde observations in China, which also indicates a water vapor maximum over the Tibetan Plateau in atmospheric columns above 500 hPa.

4.1.2. Atmospheric Circulations and Water Vapor Transports

Clearly, the unique geological feature of the plateau is responsible for this global moist distribution. To understand the dynamics and transport of moisture in the atmosphere, we calculated 59-year mean atmospheric circulations in the above two vertical sections (Figure 17d and 17e) and mean horizontal distribution of whole column water-vapor flux (Figure 18). Because of a strong contrast in the thermal property between land and ocean, the seasonal change results in a cross-south-north hemispherical monsoonal circulation. In the summer half of a year (May-October), the Tibetan Plateau acts as a strong "dynamic pump" (Wu and Zhang 1998) continuously attracts moist air from the low-latitude oceans (Figure 17d and Figure 18a). This moisture is concentrated at low-levels and transported by lower branch of atmospheric flows (Bai and Xu 2004). However, when reaching the plateau, a portion of these flows rises along the south side of the plateau, and causes frequent convections and precipitations (Xu et al. 2003). Water is transported back via surface rivers and upper-level returning flows. The other portion of water vapors is blocked by the plateau and then deflected to the east side of it and caught by the prevailing westerly wind (Figure 17e). This westerly wind transports abundant moisture to the eastern China and Asia (Figure 18a). Again, surface rivers transport downwind precipitation water back to the oceans, but at the mid and upper atmosphere, the water tower presents a "re-channel function" which constitutes a planetary-scale circulation across the east and west hemispheres. The above cross-south-north hemispheric meridional circulation and cross-east-west-hemispheric latitudinal circulation are related to the plateau's thermal and mechanical driving forcing, noticing that the upward motion starts over the Tibetan Plateau (Figure 17d-17e). The combined oceans, the plateau, surface glacier, lake, river systems, and upper-level atmospheric circulations depict a complete planetary-scale land-ocean-atmosphere water cycle on Earth. In the winter half of a year (Figure 18b, November-April), the monsoonal flows in the low-latitude oceans reverse. A persistent anticyclone occurs over the Arabian Sea along the coast of Somalia, which possesses a southwesterly flow on its northwest flank. This flow feeds more moisture into the subtropical jet coming from the Mediterranean. The further moistened westerly jet continues to transport water vapor into the plateau region and downstream region during the winter.

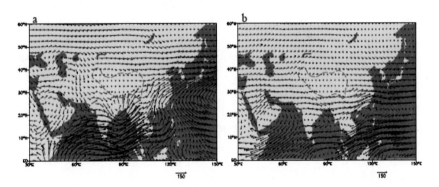

Figure 18. Horizontal distribution of 59-year averaged column water vapor flux (vectors, in kg m^{-1}s^{-1}) in the East Asian region for (a) summer and (b) winter, respectively.

4.1.3. The Plateau Cloud System and Precipitation

The Tibetan Plateau is not only a place favorable for moisture convergence, it also renders the ideal condition for moist air to condense and develop into plateau convective clouds due to its elevated land surface and strong radiative heating. Figure 17d shows the averaged summer Outgoing Long-wave Radiation (OLR) measured by satellite during 1975-2005. The summer OLR is a proxy for convective clouds. The low-value color-shaded region over the Tibetan Plateau indicates a high occurrence of convective clouds. Precipitation in the Tibetan Plateau is mainly due to these convective cloud systems.

Further analyses of a half-century observational data obtained from 9 upper-air-sounding sites and 50 surface weather stations around the Tibetan region result in a negative correlation between summer OLR and water vapor content, but a positive correlation between water vapor content and precipitation (not shown). The averaged occurrence of cumulonimbus in the Tibetan Plateau is about 345 times/year. This number is about 2.5 times higher than its surrounding area (Xu et al. 2002; Dai 1990; Flohn 1968). The frequent occurrence of convective clouds and precipitation indicates a rapid removal of water vapor from the Tibetan Plateau water-supply tank. The new moist air must fill in immediately, following the fact that this water vapor maximum in Figure 17a is presented as a climatologically persistent signal. This picture thus provides a mechanism of "constant refill" of the water tower by the atmosphere. The winter precipitations (close to 40% of total annual precipitation (Liu and Yin 2001)) will be stored as snowpacks, which provide latent water sources for summer river discharge. The summer precipitations (about 60% of total annual precipitation (Liu and Yin 2001)) will either contribute directly to the surface runoff or deposit on high mountains, depending on the variability of near-surface temperature. Because the plateau also deflects a large portion of moisture to the east (Figure 18), downstream precipitation can be an important reinforcement for large river discharge, particularly for China.

4.1.4. The Trend of Atmospheric Water Supply to the Plateau Water Tower

The present and future conditions of the Tibetan water tower concern not only a sustainable socio-economical development, but also the survivability reality for close to 40% of the world's population (UNEP, 2007). Therefore, changes in this water tower have long been the focus of scientists worldwide. It has been reported recently that a rapid melting of glaciers in many large mountains in the Tibetan Plateau region is occurring, possibly in response to the global warming (Pearce 1999; Liu and Chen 2000; Oku et al. 2006). This implies a rapid reduction of water storage in the water tower. From the atmospheric perspective, one of the important questions that need to be addressed is whether the atmosphere supply to the Tibetan water tower has experienced any change under the current warming conditions.

To answer this question, we computed a half-century (1957-2006) time series of total column of water vapor, surface temperature, and precipitation amount from historical records for the Tibetan region. In Figure 19, averaged annual variations of total water vapor content and surface temperature are plotted as the dotted curves, while fittings to these data are plotted as solid curves. The recent warming in the plateau started in the early 1970's, while the water vapor content showed an upward trend in the early 1980's and continues to the present time. The same patterns are found in the averaged annual precipitation (the blue bars in the lower panel of Figure 19). The increase of water vapor over the Tibetan Plateau may be due to following two possible mechanisms: 1) intensification of monsoonal circulation, thus a increased water vapor transport; 2) the increase of surface air temperature over the Tibetan Plateau, thus the air above it can hold more moisture.

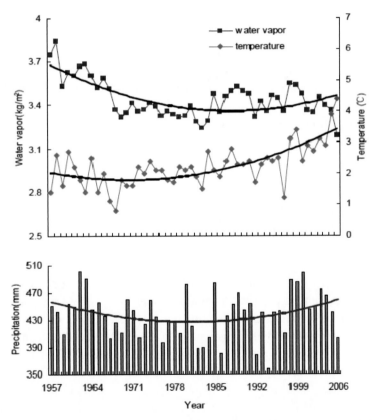

Figure 19. A 50-year time series (1957-2006) of annual mean column water vapor content (blue dotted curve), annual mean surface temperature (pink-dotted curve), and annual total precipitation (blue bars) in the Tibetan region. The solid curves are the fitting to these data.

These results suggest several possible consequences under the current warming scenario. First, owing to the combined effect of the rapid melting of glaciers and increased precipitation in the Tibetan Plateau due to global warming, the downstream transport of water from the Tibetan water tower would increase in volume. This may cause an increase in the severe flooding problems for countries along the major rivers that discharge this water. Although in China, the flooding of major rivers is typically due to downstream precipitations, the effect of Tibetan water tower runoff may aggravate the problem, causing an increase in the flooding frequency and severity in recent years (Huang et al. 2003). It was also reported that winter temperature anomaly over the northeastern Tibetan Plateau can be an important indicator for the drought and flooding conditions over India (Bansod et al. 2003). Second, the increase of surface temperature and precipitation may result in a change in the ecosystem over the plateau region. Finally, although the rapid retreat of glaciers over the plateau's mountains may pose a serious socio-economical issue for the water resources that feed 40% of the world's population, the atmosphere would present a somewhat positive response to the problem. That is, the increased atmospheric supply may alleviate the problem of rapid depletion of water resources arising from the melting of glaciers.

4.1.5. Summary

In this chapter, a persistent pool of water vapor maximum is found over the Tibetan Plateau within a layer of 500-300 hPa in the atmosphere. Although the plateau's elevated topography contributes to this pool of moisture, the low-latitude oceans play an important role in transporting water vapor from tropical oceans to the plateau region. This land – ocean - atmosphere interaction presents a complete picture of water cycles on Earth. The finding of atmospheric water vapor maximum also provides a link for the source of rich surface water storage over the Tibetan Plateau. Furthermore, the calculations for water vapor distribution and atmospheric circulation in the zonal and meridional vertical sections indicate a global-scale influence by the Tibetan Plateau, thus supporting the concept of "world water tower." That is, in the atmosphere above, a pool of concentrated water vapor takes on the role of a "water-supply tank"; at the surface, glaciers, snowpacks, and lakes serve as a "water-storage pool"; and all the rivers connecting to the plateau function as "water pipelines" that transport water away. The atmosphere also provides upper-level channels that transport water vapor in and out of the Tibetan Plateau region.

Strong surface radiative heating and topographic lifting provide favorable conditions for convection, which often results in precipitation. The frequent precipitation is crucial as a "constant refill" mechanism for the world water tower.

Based on the analyses of water vapor, clouds, precipitation, and atmospheric circulations, a schematic diagram (Figure 20) can be constructed for the concept of "the world water tower" and its hydrological function for its surrounding areas.

Finally, an analysis of a half-century time series of atmospheric water vapor content, precipitation, and surface temperature indicates that the atmospheric supply to the world water tower presents an increasing trend under recent global warming conditions. This finding implies that on one hand, the increase of water vapor content and precipitation over the Tibetan Plateau may alleviate the rapid depletion of glaciers and snowpacks due to the global warming. On the other hand, it may alter the ecosystem over the Tibetan Plateau region and may also increase severe flooding and related problems for the downstream regions.

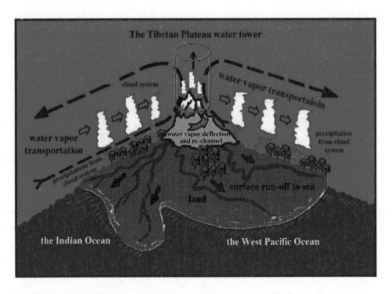

Figure 20. Schematic diagram of the Tibetan Plateau as a role in land-ocean-atmosphere interaction and hydrological cycle.

4.2. THE WATER VAPOR "RE-CHANNEL" EFFECT BY THE TIBETAN PLATEAU

In northern hemispheric summer, the southeastern part of the Tibetan Plateau peripheral region is an important moisture source and transfer region for the west boundary of the Meiyu rain belt along the Yangtze River basin. The southerly monsoon moisture flow around the southeastern skirt of the plateau from the South China Sea and the Bay of Bengal (south boundary of "large triangle" region) will turn eastwards to the Yangtze River basin, due to the topographic forcing. This branch of water vapor transport merges with another branch of moisture transport over southeastern China coming from the west edge of the subtropical high. The moisture transfer effect of the plateau played an important role in the torrential rain in the 1998 summer Yangtze River basin Meiyu belt (Xu, et al. 2002a). The total moisture budget between the south boundary inflow and east boundary outflow of the "large triangle" region is helpful in understanding the moisture source for the Meiyu rainfall along the Yangtze River basin.

4.2.1. Long-Range Moisture Transfer Model of Yangtze River Basin in Summer and Teleconnection of Source/Sink Structure

The moisture budget in the mainland of China obviously varies with season. The maximum monthly net moisture inflow occurs in May, June, and July. During this period, the summer monsoon prevails over southern China at first, then enters the Yangtze River basin and starts to influence northern China. When the summer monsoon reaches its maximum intensity in central China, the southwesterly (or southerly) wind carrying a large amount of moisture enters the mainland of China (Liu 1997). Chen et al. (1991) pointed out that the moisture inflow for summer precipitation in China comes mainly from the tropical South China Sea, secondly from the Bay of Bengal, and thirdly from the southeast monsoon associated with the Pacific subtropical high ridge. Similar climatic features of summer moisture transport were found by Xu et al. (2003) in their computational results from the NCEP/NCAR reanalysis data. However, the moisture transport distribution feature in the period from the middle June to July in 1998 was somewhat different from the climatic mean circumstance. The southwestly flow from the Bay of Bengal is strengthened since the middle June, but the southeastly flow from the west ridge of the Pacific subtropical high became even more prominent; in July, two prominent southerly flow from the Indian Ocean and the Bay of Bengal became the main body of the moisture flow.

The whole-column moisture transport in the influential domain of China in summer season and its summer climatic mean was shown in Figure 21. The moisture transport feature in the "large triangle" key region was also depicted, which identified that major moisture transport sources were from the Indian Ocean, the South China Sea, and the Western Pacific, and all these moisture transports converge to the south of the plateau. There is a key scientific question regarding the genesis of the Meiyu rainband, i.e., why is there the continuous convergence of a great amount of moisture in the Yangtze River basin in the Meiyu period? Does the persistent torrential rainfall during the Meiyu season mean that there is a particular teleconnection source/sink structure in the Yangtze River basin? This structure reflects the summer moisture flow pattern in the regions of the South China Sea and the Bay of Bangle-Tibetan Plateau-Yangtze River basin.

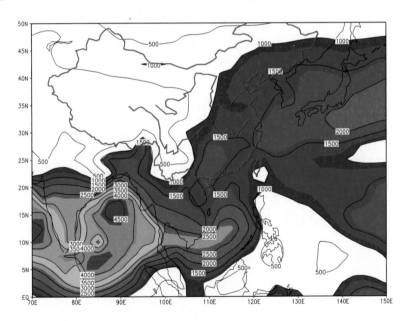

Figure 21. Summer climatic mean whole-column moisture flux field
(unit: g· cm^{-1}· s^{-1}).

4.2.2. The Inverse Flow Patterns of Moisture Transport during Drought/Flooding Years

To examine the moisture transport path and teleconnection structure of water vapor fluxes between low-latitude oceans and responsive area in eastern China, particularly in the Yangtze River basin, we computed the anomaly of whole-column water-vapor fluxes in East Asian region for drought and flooding years, respectively. In Figure 22a, we plotted whole-column water vapor fluxes during the flooding years in eastern China.

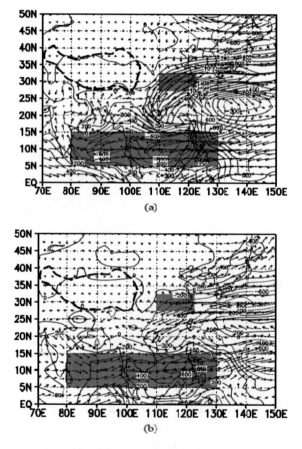

Figure 22. The anomalies of the column-integrated water vapor flux (contours and arrows) in summer for (a) flooding years of 1980, 1983, 1991, and 1998, and (b) drought years of 1978, 1981, 1985, and 1986 using NCEP-NCAR reanalysis data. The thick dash lines outline the area of Tibetan Plateau. The shaded areas show a teleconnection structure between low-latitude oceans and midlatitude land.

One can see that northward transports of water vapor were present on the south side of the Tibetan Plateau. These northward transports of water vapor were related to the westward transport of moisture in the low-latitude oceans. The Tibetan Plateau blocked these moisture fluxes and deflected them to the east. The water vapor continued to travel northeastward, and eventually converged in the Yangtze River basin with northerly flows carrying moisture from North Pacific. The two shaded regions indicate a teleconnection pattern between low-latitude oceans and midlatitude moisture anomaly.

In contrast, in Figure 22b, the anomaly of whole-column water vapor fluxes is plotted for the drought years in eastern China. It is clear that the flow pattern with moisture transport is completely reversed. The most noticeable feature is that the northward transport of water vapor on the south side of the Tibetan Plateau is completely missing. The inverse of water vapor fluxes in the low-latitude oceans and in eastern China is remarkable. This reflects a shift of teleconnection pattern to an exact opposite phase.

The comparative analyses of vector fields suggest the eastward transports of moisture flux are closely related to the moisture from southern oceans, which pushed the moisture forward to the north toward the plateau and transferred eastwards to the Yangtze River basin. It is quite contrary in drought years that the moisture flux from the ocean cannot reach the plateau and hence does not have an eastward transferred process in an easterly prevailing environment in the Yangtze River region. It implies that the moisture effect of the plateau in the north part of "large triangle" region is quite important for the Meiyu rainfall along the Yangtze River basin.

4.2.3. Correlation Vector Field Features of Moisture Flux over the Yangtze River Basin

Based on the anomaly analysis of the summer whole-column moisture flux in the Yangtze River basin, the inverse phase of moisture flux distributions in drought/flood years is revealed. In order to further clarify the moisture transport in the Yangtze River basin "source/sink" structure, the correlation vector method is used to trace moisture sources and moisture transport tracks. The correlation vector is expressed as

$$R(x, y) = Ru\ (x, y)i + Rv\ (x, y)j, \tag{1}$$

where **R** is the composite correlation vector of u- and v-components of whole-column moisture flux, *qu* and *qv*, and *Ru* and *Rv* are component correlation fields for *qu* and *qv* respectively. Figure 23 shows the composite correlation vector field of *qu* and *qv*. It can be seen from Figure 23 that the main part of the southern branch of moisture flow for summer Yangtze River basin flood can be traced to the low-latitude Western Pacific, South China Sea, and Indian Ocean. This southern branch moisture flow (correlation vector field) passes through the plateau to transfer towards the Yangtze River basin, converges with strong northerly flows, then further on crosses Japanese Sea.

The above south and north moisture flows form a long narrow zonal moisture convergence belt in the Yangtze River basin. Therefore, the confluence of south and north moisture flow is important in the formation of the moisture source/sink structure of the Yangtze River basin Meiyu belt. The composite correlation vector field indicates that the south branch moisture flow in the "large triangle" region and north branch of moisture flow in the Japanese Sea reflect the moisture transport flow pattern of the Meiyu belt resulted from the interaction of plateau land-ocean-atmosphere processes. The warm/moist south branch flow originated from low-latitude oceans and cool/wet north branch flow from middle-high-latitude oceans meet in the Yangtze River basin, and form a flow confluent belt of high humidity, which is responsible for heavy rains in Eastern China and other East Asian countries.

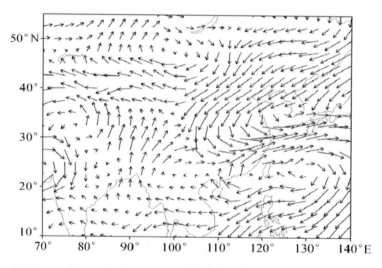

Figure 23. Composite correlation vector field of whole layer moisture fluxes (*qu*, *qv*) in summer along the Yangtze River basin.

4.2.4. Water Vapor Budget and Characteristic of Water Vapor Transport

From previous analyses, it becomes clear that two processes contribute to flooding situation in the Yangtze River basin in eastern China. The first one is the formation of mesoscale convective systems (MCSs) over the Tibetan Plateau. These MCSs move eastward and out of the plateau, which further develop into "lee cyclones." The second process is the continuous supply of moisture to eastern China from the low-latitude oceans. In the latter process, the Tibetan Plateau serves two roles in the water vapor transport. First, as a heat source, the plateau acts as an air pump that attracts low-latitude warm-moist air coming up towards the Tibetan Plateau. Second, due to the high-rise of the plateau, it blocks and deflects a large amount of water vapor to the east. Therefore, in this sense, the Tibetan Plateau serves as role of a water vapor "re-channel station" (Xu and Tao 2002).

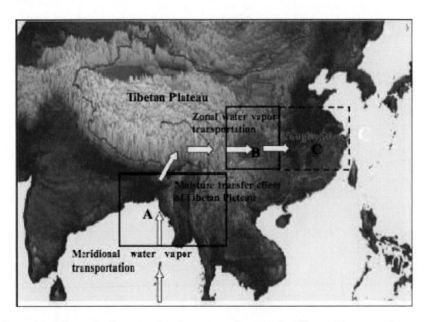

Figure 24. Schematic diagram of moisture transfer over the Tibetan Plateau and moisture-budget key areas (A , B , C) for Meiyu rainfall in the Yangtze River basin.

These two roles of the Tibetan Plateau in the water vapor transport are clearly depicted in Figure 24. In this figure, the southerly transport of water vapor takes place in region A (15°-25°N, 80°-100°E), while the re-channeled water vapor is found in region B (25°-35°N, 100-110E). Water vapor finally deposit in region C (25°-35°N, 110°-120°E) as forms of precipitation. To support this view, following statistical calculations are performed.

1) The Interannual Variability of the Meridional and Zonal Transport of Water Vapor in the Peripheral Region of the Tibetan Plateau

Based on above characteristics of water transport around the Tibetan Plateau (Figure 24), we can treat the transport on the south side of the plateau as qv, while on the east side of the plateau as qu. The whole-column (from the surface to 300-hPa pressure level) water vapor transports corresponding to these two components can be expressed as

$$Q_u(x, y, t) = \frac{1}{g} \int_{300}^{P_s} q(x, y, p, t) u(x, y, p, t) dp \qquad (2)$$

$$Q_v(x, y, t) = \frac{1}{g} \int_{300}^{P_s} q(x, y, p, t) v(x, y, p, t) dp \qquad (3)$$

where q is specific humidity, and u and v are two horizontal wind components.

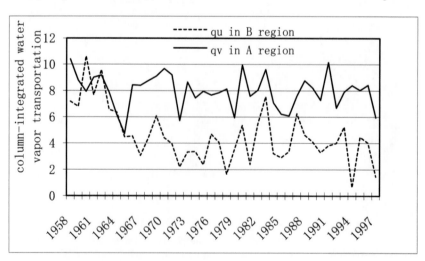

Figure 25. Interannual variability of whole-layer moisture flux components for key areas (A : qv ,B : qu) around the Plateau.

We used U.S. National Center for Environmental Prediction and National Center for Atmospheric Research reanalysis data to compute the interannual variability of water vapor transports qv in region A and qu in region B. These two quantities are plotted in Figure 25. One can see that qv and qu in two different regions displayed very similar interannual variability. They have very similar phase variations. In fact, the correlation coefficients for these two variables reached 0.36 with a 0.95 confidence level. This result indicates that water vapor transport in the vicinity of the Tibetan Plateau experiences a transition from one direction to another direction. That is, under the plateau orographic forcing, the southerly water vapor transport on the south side of the plateau becomes an eastward transport on the east side of the plateau.

2) Correlation between Zonal and Meridional Water Vapor Transports

To further verify that the above two components of water vapor transports are related, we compute correlation between a component transport and all transports from the other component for East Asian region. Figure 26 plots all the zonal water vapor transports correlated with the southerly water vapor flux in region A (in the box). Two high-valued bands (with opposite signs) occurred northeast and southeast of the southerly water vapor flux. The northeast band represents a correlated water vapor transport eastward in the mid- to lower- reach of the Yangtze River basin. This feature is consistent with above "re-channeled" effect of the Tibetan Plateau.

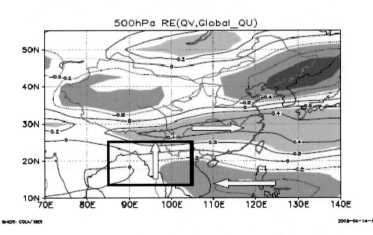

Figure 26. Correlation fields of moisture flux qv component in the key area A (the square area) with the qu component in Asian region (shaded areas denote the correlation is significant to a confidence level more than 0. 9). Red counters outline China land area with two major rivers: Yangzhi and Yellow rivers.

The southeast band represents a water vapor supply (a westward transport) from the western Pacific and South China Sea to region A, where the transport turns to a northward transport.

Figure 27 shows all the meridional water vapor transports correlated with the westerly water vapor flux in region C (in the box). One can see that two large-valued regions (with opposite signs) were located northwest and southwest of the westerly vapor flux in the lower reach of the Yangtze River. This result indicates that water vapor transport in the Yangtze River basin is related the convergence and confluence of the northerly and southerly water vapor fluxes. The convergence of these two fluxes leads to a westerly water vapor transport further eastward.

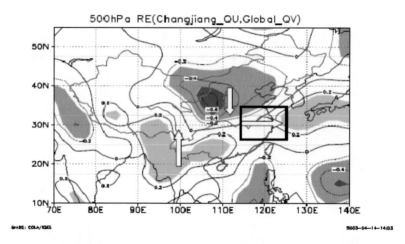

Figure 27. Correlation fields of moisture flux qu component of the mid- and lower-reaches of Yangtze River basin (the square area) with the qv component in Asian region (shaded areas denote the correlation is significant to a confidence level more than 0. 9).

3) Water Vapor Budget in the Yangtze River Basin

As denoted in Figure 24, region C covers mid- and lower-reaches of the Yangtze River basin, where Meiyu rainfall is mainly located. We now calculate water vapor budget in "box C" using

$$Q_W = \sum_{y=\phi_1}^{\phi_2} Q_u(\lambda_1, y, t) \quad Q_E = \sum_{y=\phi_1}^{\phi_2} Q_u(\lambda_2, y, t)$$

$$Q_S = \sum_{x=\lambda_1}^{\lambda_2} Q_u(x,\phi_1,t) \quad Q_N = \sum_{x=\lambda_1}^{\lambda_2} Q_u(x,\phi_2,t)$$

and

$$Q_T = Q_W - Q_E + Q_S - Q_N \tag{4}$$

where Q_W, Q_E, Q_S, and Q_N are the water vapor fluxes at west, east, south, and north boundaries of "box C," and Q_T is the net water vapor deposit inside "box C," and $\varphi1$,$\varphi2$,$\lambda1$,$\lambda2$ are the latitudes and longitudes for corresponding boundaries.

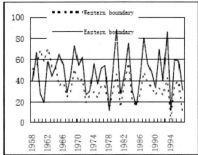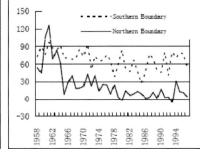

Figure28. Interannual variability of moisture budget at the boundaries of Middle and Lower Reaches of Yangtze River basin (a. East and west , b. North and south).

Figure 28 shows the interannual variability of moisture fluxes in and out of "box C." It can be seen that the west and south boundaries act as the major in-flux boundaries (positive values indicate flows from west to east, and from south to north), while east boundary is mainly an out-flux boundary, and the north boundary behaves both in and out-flux boundary. Combined with Figs. 25-28, we conclude that the water vapor transports in region A from low-latitude oceans in the south, turns eastward into region B when reaching the plateau, and then further transports into region C. Besides flowing in on the west side, there are also moisture fluxes entering from south (from low-latitude oceans) and from north (from northwest Pacific), while the moisture either fallout as precipitation or transport out the box through the eastern boundary. This picture is consistent with the source/sink teleconnection model of Meiyu rainfall in Xu and Chen (2003).

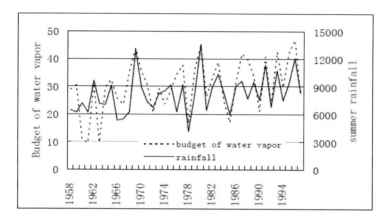

Figure 29. The interannual variability of summer precipitation and net water vapor budget in the mid- and lower- reaches of the Yangtze River basin.

Further analysis of the above "box model," we found that the net amount of moisture deposit in region C presented a very similar interannual variability to that of the total precipitation in this region (Figure 29). The correlation coefficients reached 0.715 with a confidence level of 0.99. Therefore, the water vapor budget in region C provides a key indicator for the Yangtze River basin flooding potential.

4) Correlation between Water Vapor Budget and Zonal and Meridional Water Vapor Transports

We further compute the correlation between the net deposit of water vapor in box C and all meridional transport in East Asia (Figure 30a). It can be seen that the water vapor budget in the mid- to lower-reaches of Yangtze River is related to two branches of transport of moisture. One branch is associated with southerly transport on the southeast side of the Tibetan Plateau. The other branch is coming from south China. The correlation between the net deposit of water vapor in box C and all zonal transport in East Asia is shown in Figure 30b. In this case, three bands of zonal moisture transport are relevant to the water vapor budget in the Yangtze River basin: the westward transport in the low-latitude oceans, from the western Pacific to South China Sea to the Bay of Bangle; the eastward transport in the Tibetan Plateau and along the Yangtze River; and westward transport at higher midlatitude, from the northwest Pacific to northern China. All these results are consistent with previous analyses, suggesting a teleconnection structure of moisture source/sink for East Asian monsoonal rainfall.

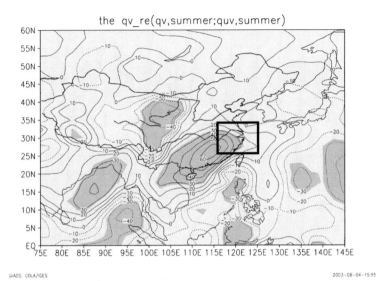

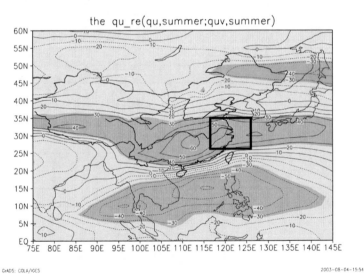

Figure 30. Correlation fields of moisture budget in box C of the mid- and lower-reaches of the Yangtze River basin (the square area) with (a) the meridional, and (b) zonal components of whole-layer water vapor flux (shaded areas denote the correlation is significant to a confidence level more than 0. 9).

Chapter 5

THE RESPONSE OF ASIAN SUMMER MONSOONAL PRECIPITATION TO THE CHANGE OF APPARENT HEATING SOURCE OVER THE TIBETAN PLATEAU

It is well documented that the Asian summer monsoon has been experiencing a steady weakening trend in recent decades. Since the Asian summer monsoon is the largest and most pronounced monsoon in the world, its change in strength may exert a profound impact on global weather and climate systems, especially on the rainfall pattern in South and East Asia. On the other hand, as a vast elevated landmass, the Tibetan Plateau forms a huge heating source protruding into the free atmosphere. Setting against the backdrop of global climate change, whether or not does the change of this heating affect the change of Asian summer monsoon and thus rainfall distribution? Here we show that the apparent heat source over the Tibetan Plateau is closely correlated with the Asian summer monsoonal circulation, and that the weakening of the Asian summer monsoon is logically associated with the decreasing trend of the Tibetan Plateau apparent heat source. Further analysis indicates that the change of rainfall pattern in China in recent decades is consistent with the decreasing of the Asian summer monsoon.

5.1. THE HEAT SOURCE INDUCED
BY THE TIBETAN PLATEAU

Figure 31a shows 62-years (1948-2009) averaged south-north vertical cross section of the Tibetan Plateau (dark brown) and related apparent heating (the definition of which will be given in the following section; color-shaded in unit of degrees of Celsius) averaged over $95^O E \sim 100^O E$. Figure 1b shows the same plot for east-west vertical cross section (averaged over $30^O N \sim 35^O N$). One can see that large heating sources are formed in the free atmosphere in conjunction with the elevated land surfaces, which will undoubtedly exert a profound impact on the global atmospheric circulations. One of the unique roles of the heating source associated with the Tibetan Plateau is to regulate global water vapor transport, the subtle change of which can lead to a large area drought or flood in many parts of the world. In fact, the Tibetan Plateau plays a role of "the world water tower" (Xu et al. 2009). The related change in water resources and environmental in this region will affect socio-economical development for almost 40% of world population.

The Asian summer monsoon is responsible for warm-season precipitation across most South and East Asia. In recent decades, it has been observed that the Asian summer monsoon circulation exhibits an appreciable decreasing trend (Jiang et al. 2005; Ding et al. 2010). In response to this change, the precipitation pattern in East Asia also experiences significant changes (Zhou et al. 2008; Ashfaq et al. 2009).

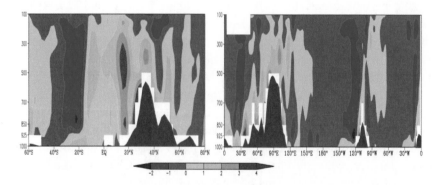

Figure 31. Vertical cross-sections of land surface elevations and summer (March-August) apparent heating (in unit of $°C.d^{-1}$) averaged over 1948-2009: (a) South-north view (average between 95°E~100°E); and (b) East-west view (average between 30°N~35°N).

Numerous studies have been conducted over the last decade or so to explain what causes the weakening of the Asian summer monsoon. Using the U.S. National Center for Atmospheric Research (NCAR) community atmospheric model version 3 (CAM3) and National Oceanic and Atmospheric Administration (NOAA) Geophysical Physical Fluid Dynamics Laboratory (GFDL) atmospheric model version 2.1 (AM2.1), Li et al. (2008) report that the recent warming in the Tropics, especially the warming associated with the tropical inter-decadal variability centered over the central and eastern Pacific, is a primary cause for the weakening of the Asian summer monsoon since the late 1970s. Lu and Dong (2008) attributed the weakening of the Asian summer monsoon to the weakening of Atlantic thermohaline circulation. Yu et al. (2004) found that the weakening of the Asian summer monsoon corresponded well to the cooling trend in the upper troposphere around 300hPa in the East Asian region. However, all of these studies bypassed an important question, that is, what is the role of the Tibetan Plateau in the weakening of the Asian summer monsoon? As many studies have shown that the Tibetan Plateau serves as a main driving force for the Asian summer monsoon (Wu and Zhang 1998; Xu et al. 2010), does the change of the monsoonal circulation reflect the change of the heat source induced by the Tibetan Plateau?

We first calculate the apparent heat source over the Tibetan Plateau. Following Yanai and Johnson (1993) and Yanai and Tomita (1998), the apparent heat source is defined as

$$Q_1 = c_p [\frac{\partial T}{\partial t} + V \cdot \nabla T + (\frac{p}{p_0})^\kappa \omega \frac{\partial \theta}{\partial p}] \tag{1}$$

where T is air temperature, $V=(u, v)$ horizontal wind vector, p pressure, ω vertical velocity, θ potential temperature, and $p_0=1000$ hPa.

The color background in Figure 32 indicates land elevation in the eastern hemisphere. The Tibetan Plateau region is marked by dark red, where the average land elevation exceeds 4000 m. The rectangle encompasses the area where Q_1 is calculated.

Next we calculate a whole-column moisture transfer vector, whose components are defined as

$$q_u(x,y,t) = \frac{1}{g} \int_{300}^{P_s} q(x,y,p,t)u(x,y,p,t)dp, \tag{2}$$

$$q_v(x,y,t) = \frac{1}{g} \int_{300}^{P_s} q(x,y,p,t)v(x,y,p,t)dp, \qquad\qquad (3)$$

where g is gravitational acceleration, (u, v) are respectively the zonal and meridional wind components, q the specific humidity, and P_s the surface pressure.

With these defined physical variables, we can calculate the correlation between the apparent heat source over the Tibetan Plateau and the water vapor fluxes. The data used in the calculation is 2.5x2.5 degree latitude and longitude reanalysis data generated by U.S. National Center for Environmental Prediction–National Center for Atmospheric Research (Kalnay et al. 1996). For precipitation analysis, we use a half-century surface precipitation observational data archived at China Meteorological Administration and CRU (the University of East Anglia Climatic Research Unit) monthly precipitation data (spatial resolution of $0.5° \times 0.5°$ and covering the period 1901–2000) (New et al. 2002).

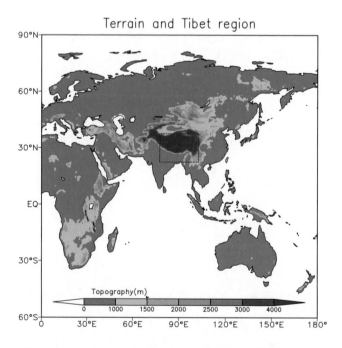

Figure 32. Surface elevation (color shaded) and the Tibetan Plateau region (dashed rectangle) where the apparent hear source is calculated (based on Eq. 1).

5.2. CORRELATION BETWEEN THE TIBETAN HEAT SOURCE AND MOISTURE TRANSPORT

Figure 33 is the calculated horizontal distribution of correlation vector between the apparent heat source over the Tibetan Plateau and the whole column water vapor flux averaged over March-August of 1948-2009. The yellow (or green) color highlights the positive (or negative) areas that passed the 90% significance tests for the correlations. The northward correlation vectors in the yellow region in the south of the Tibetan Plateau, especially in the Bay of Bangle, represent water vapor fluxes that are "pumped up" by the heat source of the Tibetan Plateau. These vectors then turn slightly eastward, becoming the classical southwestly moisture fluxes of the East Asian summer monsoon. From the distribution of these correlation vectors, one can clearly see that the heat source over the Tibetan Plateau (Q_1) correlated well with the Asian summer monsoonal flow.

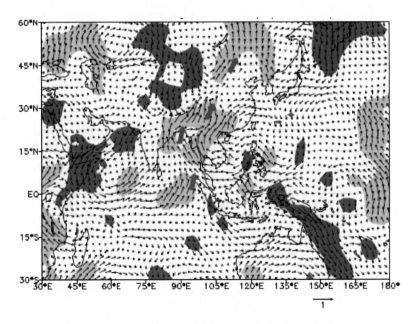

Figure 33. Horizontal distribution of correlation vector between atmospheric apparent heat source (Q_1) over the Tibetan Plateau and the whole column water vapor flux (q_u and q_v) averaged over March-August of 1948-2009. The yellow or green color highlights the positive or negative areas that passed the 90% significance tests for the correlations.

5.3. Variations of Apparent Heat Source over the Tibetan Plateau and Anomalous East Asian Monsoonal Flows

The above result simply re-demonstrates the classic description of the Tibetan Plateau acting as a heat source to drive the monsoonal circulation.

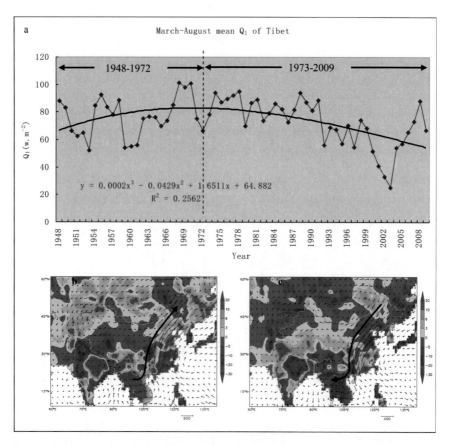

Figure 34. (a) Annual variation of the averaged March-August apparent heat sources (Q_1) over the Tibetan Plateau (blue curve). The solid black curve is the fitting to annual variation, indicating the long-term trend of the apparent heating over the Tibetan Plateau. The corresponding anomalies in whole-column water vapor flux (vectors) and March-August precipitation amount (color shaded) in the period of (b) 1948-1972; and (c) 1973-2009 are displayed (relative to 1948-2009 average). The black-solid arrows indicate the major directions of the anomalies of water vapor transport during the two time periods.

We now examine how this heat source has changed in the last sixty years. Figure 34a shows the time series of Q_1 from 1948 to 2009. The fitted average of this heat source is marked by the solid curve, depicting the multi-decadal trend of this field. It is clearly seen that since early 1970s, the Tibetan Plateau apparent heat source has presented a decreasing trend. In contrast, before early 1970s, this field displays an increasing trend.

If we divide these sixty years into two periods, one from 1948 to 1972, and one from 1973 to 2009, we can calculate the anomalies of water vapor fluxes and summer precipitations corresponding to these two time periods respectively. The anomalies in the two periods displayed almost exactly opposite patterns (Figure 34b vs. 34c). During the period of strengthening of the Tibetan apparent heat source (1948-1972), the water vapor fluxes display a normal monsoonal flow pattern, similar to that shown in Figure 33. However, corresponding to the decreasing period (1973-2009) of the apparent heat source over the Tibetan Plateau, northeastly water vapor fluxes in the eastern China and the Bay of Bangle are found, which present an anti-monsoonal flow pattern. During this period, southeast and west China are abnormally wet, whereas Northeast China extending all the way to the Southeast Asian Peninsula presents an abnormally dry pattern. These results imply that the decreasing trend of apparent heat source over the Tibetan Plateau is a possible cause for the weakening of Asian summer monsoon. In response to this weakening of monsoon, the entire Asian continent may experience abnormal rainfall patterns.

5.4. LONG-TERM TREND OF PRECIPITATION DISTRIBUTION OVER CHINA

Finally, we carefully computed the summer precipitation change rate during 1973-2009, shown in Figure 35. The red (blue) dots indicate a positive (negative) change rate, while the size of the dots depicts the amount of rainfall change over a decade (change rate). The precipitation trend in China displays three distinctive regions. Region *A* presents a "strong wet-trend" area; region *B* presents a "strong dry-trend" area; and region *C* presents a "weak wet-trend" area. The trend of rain-suppression in the *B* belt is consistent with the decreasing of southwesterly moisture transport, corresponding to the weakening of East Asian monsoonal circulation.

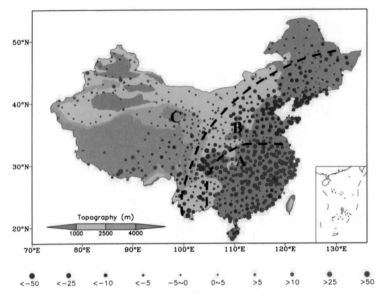

Figure 35. The distribution of interdecadal change rate of summer precipitation in China during the period of 1957-2006 (unit: mm/decade). The data is from 753 meteorological observational stations in China. The color and size of the dots denote positive/negative and magnitude of the change rate. Color-shaded areas indicate the topography.

5.5. SUMMARY

In this chapter, we analyzed correlation between the heat source over the Tibetan Plateau and moisture transport due to Asian summer monsoon. Further analysis of the long-term trend of the apparent heat source over the Tibetan Plateau seems to indicate that the change of the heat source results in two different anomalous monsoonal flows. In particular, the decreasing trend of the apparent heat source over the Tibetan Plateau in recent four decades may be responsible for the weakening of Asian summer monsoon.

In response to the weakening of Asian summer monsoon, China's precipitation presents a pattern with three-trend regions. The rain-diminishing region is consistent with the decreased moisture transport due to the weakening of Asian summer monsoon, which forms a dry-trend belt in the north and central China. This result may have a profound implication for China's environment and sustainability developments.

Chapter 6

A New Integrated Observational System over the Tibetan Plateau

The above analyses reveal that many storms and weather systems in Eastern China and East Asia are closely related to the signals from upstream regions. In particular, many convective cloud clusters are generated over the Tibetan Plateau and transported downstream. These convective systems may further intensify as they gain more "lee vorticity" coming down from the plateau. In addition, the Tibet Plateau plays a very important role in Asian summer monsoon. It attracts moisture from low-latitude oceans and re-channels the moisture eastward to the Yangtze River basin, supporting the development of extreme weather systems.

Consequently, the Tibetan Plateau is considered as one of the most active and sensitive regions for atmosphere-land-ocean interaction in the world. Close monitoring and accurate observations of energy and water cycle in this region will provide invaluable information for warning and prediction of downstream weather development and climate change. Now the question is how we can set up an observing and monitoring system upstream in the key regions, such as the Tibetan Plateau. Such a monitoring system is crucial for providing early warning and accurate prediction of disastrous weather downstream. For this reason, Chinese and Japanese governments have jointly invested a large amount of resources to establish a set of comprehensive monitoring platforms and observational stations over the Tibetan Plateau. This project has been carried out since 2005. In 2009, the established observational network has formally become an operational network. In this study, we will describe how this observing network can provide warning and prediction capability for disastrous weather in East Asia. The complete datasets may also be useful for studying the impact of the Tibetan Plateau on global weather and climate change. We will mostly concentrate on scientific issues about the impacts of upstream environmental information on prediction and warning of downstream disastrous weather.

6.1. SCIENTIFIC BACKGROUND

In 1979, China carried out a field experiment to investigate the role of the Tibetan Plateau in the global atmospheric circulation. It was this experiment that provided, for the first time, a qualitative understanding of general aspects of Tibetan Plateau meteorology and its role in the Asian Monsoon. In 1998, Chinese and Japanese scientists jointly conducted the second atmospheric science experiment over the plateau, under the sponsorship of GAME/Tibet, TiPEX, and CAMP/Tibet (Ma et al. 2008). Significant progress was made during these experiments. Improved descriptions of the Tibetan Plateau's land–atmospheric interaction and various hydrometeorological processes have been studied quantitatively using more sophisticated datasets and modeling tools. These research activities and field experiments are now being extended into a new phase: the Tibetan Observation and Research Platform (TORP), discussed in (Ma et al. 2008). With the understanding of the Tibetan Plateau's importance in the regional and global atmospheric circulations gained from these field experiments, it is highly desirable to establish a set of more permanent and operational observing networks. Consequently, a New Integrated Observational System over the Tibetan Plateau (NIOST), supported by the Chinese–Japanese joint international cooperation program, was initiated and has been implemented since 2005. The Chinese Academy of Meteorological Sciences (CAMS) of the China Meteorological Administration (CMA) is implementing the NIOST project. NIOST will provide a mechanism for transferring the research results from field experiments into a forecast capability, as well as for enhancing research activities by providing routinely available and long-term data sets.

The key scientific issues addressed by NIOST are 1) the predictability of disastrous weather in East China and the East Asian countries with upstream information in the Tibetan region; 2) the role of the geographic structure of the plateau in regional and global energy and water circulations; and 3) the global and climate change issues related to the Tibetan Plateau. NIOST should also have a great impact on the meteorological and hydrological operations and technical development in these areas, such as the enhancement of numerical weather prediction, development of scientific infrastructure and training of a new generation of scientists, and improvement of PBL parameterizations over the plateau and data analysis/assimilation tools. Based on these analyses, an observational network in two lines was designed (shown in Figure 36): the east–west array of an observing network located on the south side of the Tibetan Plateau, and the north–south array of an observing network located on the east side of the plateau.

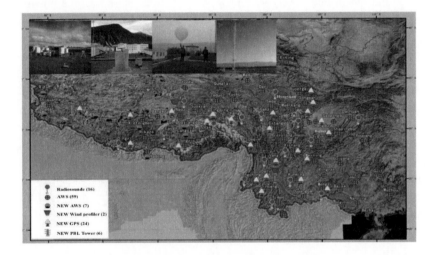

Figure 36. The designed and implemented observing network for NIOST. The top picture panels are examples of a wind profiler station, a GPS observing station, an upper-air sounding site, and a PBL tower, respectively. The green lines indicate the designed east–west and north–south array of NIOST observing networks.

The observational network covers most of the Tibetan Plateau, a large portion of the Yunnan province (on the southeast side of Tibet), and some portions of Sichuang, Guangxi, and other provinces along the Yangtze River Basin. The observational network is composed of several observing platforms, including GPS, GPS sounding (radiosondes with GPS tracking), automated weather stations (AWS), PBL towers, wind profilers, and satellites. The 16 GPS sounding sites provide vertical column observations for basic meteorological elements: wind, temperature, pressure, and moisture. The dense GPS network consisting of 24 stations provides a relatively complete monitoring of column water vapor data in Tibet and adjacent regions. The surface energy budget, comprising surface net radiation and sensible and latent heat fluxes, is measured from six PBL towers. The 66 AWS stations provide surface meteorological measurements. Two regional wind profiler stations provide additional wind information. Assimilation of FY2C (Chinese weather satellite) data is also planned.

6.2. IMPLEMENTATION

Beginning in late 2005, we developed a general observational network in the Tibetan Plateau and its surrounding areas, a satellite observing system for East Asian water vapor monitoring, and a regional climate and mesoscale modeling system suitable for land-surface characteristics over the plateau. In 2006, we initially implemented a water vapor real-time observational network, a land–atmospheric interaction observational network, and an observational data processing and archiving system. In 2007, data analyses began on high-impact weather in China and East Asia, water resources and water circulation over the Tibetan Plateau and its surroundings, and forecast skill improvement related to socioeconomic benefits. This ensemble of research, development, and operational activities will be carried out through 2009. At that time, the project will be evaluated and recommendations will be made for NIOST's transition to an operational system after 2009.

6.3. REAL -TIME DATA PROCESSING
AND OBSERVATION OPERATION

The real-time data processing of NIOST is shown in Figure 37a. Local operational centers in the southwestern provinces and Xizang (Tibet), an autonomous region of China, are responsible for collecting and quality-controlling the observational data. These data are then sent to the headquarters in Beijing for further processing and analyses. Various end products are generated from the data. The corresponding data communication and processing flow are shown in Figure 37b. In 2009, two data processing and archive centers will be established—one in CMA/CAMS in Beijing, China and the other in the University of Tokyo in Japan.

NIOST focuses on the development of an operational observing network combining surface observations on meteorological, hydrological, and surface energy fields with upper-level atmospheric soundings.

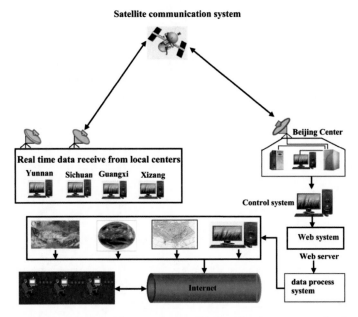

Figure 37a. NIOST project implementation and data collection, communication, and processing systems and platforms.

Data communication and processing flow chart

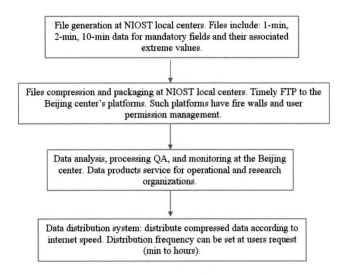

Figure 37b. Flow chart of the NIOST data communication and processing.

The developed observing network may provide crucial meteorological information that can be used for monitoring, prediction, and assessment of high-impact weather and climate change for East Asia, including China and Japan. The new observational datasets may also be useful when studying the impact of the Tibetan Plateau on global weather and climate change.

Chapter 7

PREDICTION OF SNOWSTORMS USING UPSTREAM WEATHER SIGNALS

The implement of a new integrated observing system over the Tibetan Plateau (NIOST) is based on the premise that the observing and monitoring system can improve the forecasts of extreme weather downstream. In this chapter, we discuss one application how the information obtained from NIOST can be utilized to provide a warning and forecasting of China 2008 grand snowstorms.

7.1. CHINA 2008 GRAND SNOWSTORMS

From early January to early February 2008, China experienced once-in-50-years (or once-in-100-years for some regions) snow and ice storms. The snowstorms paralyzed both surface and air communications, cut off electricity and other energy transportations, and damaged agricultural crops. Even worse, these storms occurred right before the Chinese traditional New Year (February 5), when more than two hundred million people were on the move to their homes or on holiday trips. The storms trapped millions of people in the railway stations, airport, and other transportation shelters. According to Chinese Department of Civil and Internal Affair, more than 100 million people suffered from these storms, and the economical loss totaled about 100 billion Chinese Yuan (about 15 billion U.S. dollars).

The snowstorms occurred in such a grand scale that 20 out of China's 34 provinces and special districts were affected by this disastrous event. These snow and ice storms were organized into four episodes, occurring respectively during 10-16 January, 18-22 January, 25-29 January, and 31 January to 2 February. Most of southeast China was impacted by these grand-scale storms. Figure 38 shows the distribution of accumulated total precipitation during this period (10 January-2 February) over China. There were 7 provinces had 500 mm (~20 in) total snowfall during this period. Figure 21 also plots the distribution of snowfall and freezing rain areas. It is seen that most snowstorms occurred in the north, which gradually transitioned into freezing rains in the south. The affected areas covered from southeast to central-east China. Based on these observations, we plot regional precipitation and temperature variations during 10 January-3 February, averaged over stations east of 105°E within a latitudinal band of 25°N-35°N (Figure 39). The figure shows that four significant precipitation episodes occurred during this period, accompanied by a sustaining low temperature, which experienced a dramatic drop during the first precipitation episode.

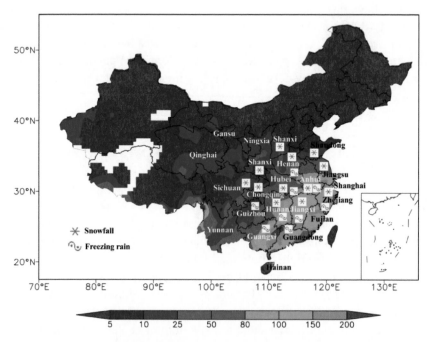

Figure 38. Distribution of accumulated total precipitation during China 2008 grand snowstorms between 10 January to 2 February 2008 (unit: mm) as well as the major snowfall and freezing rain areas. To convert to snow depth, the number should be divided by a snow-liquid conversion factor of 0.1-0.2.

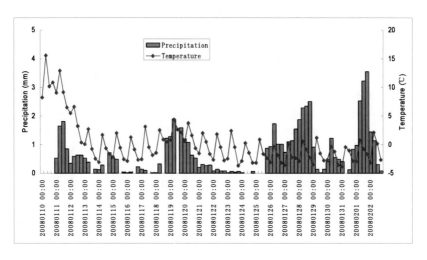

Figure 39. Time evolution of precipitation and surface air temperature, averaged over a storm region (east of 105°E in a latitudinal belt of 25°N-35°N) during 10 January-3 February 2008 (time is in UTC).

6.2. SCIENTIFIC BACKGROUND

Studies for China winter snowstorms began to occur in the 1970's. Wang and Xu (1979) first investigated China's Inner Mongolia "77.10" extraordinary snowstorm. They proposed a "north ridge-south trough" anti-phased conceptual model for snowstorms in northern China. Wang and Ding (1995) discussed the possible role of moist symmetric instability in the formation of "86.11" snowstorm in northern China. Gong (2001) analyzed the relationship between Inner Mongolia snowstorms and low-level jets, and pointed out the importance of southerly low-level jets in the development of snowstorms in this region. Many other researchers also carried out diagnostic and modeling studies on snowstorms over the Tibetan Plateau (Deng et al. 2000; Zhang et al. 2000; Wang et al. 2002). In recent years, there have been some case studies on abnormal snowstorms in the lower latitudes of southern China. For example, Zhu and Shou (1994) investigated secondary circulation and frontogenesis associated with a snowstorm occurred in the Yangtze and Huai River basins. Yang et al. (2006) also conducted a modeling study of this storm using the MM5 model. Nevertheless, knowledge for snowstorms occurred in southern China is still quite limited. Specially, the physical understanding for abnormal winter precipitation in lower latitude and southern China is largely insufficient.

It is well known that water vapor supply is an important condition for precipitation. In China, many scientists have concentrated on water vapor transport associated with Asian monsoon system (Xu 1958; Lu and Gao 1983; Chen and Yen 1988; Huang et al. 1998). Xu et al. (2002a) and Xu et al. (2003) pointed out that the Tibetan Plateau served as a "re-channel station" for water vapor, coming from South China Sea and Indian Ocean and transporting to the Yangtze River basin. Recently, He et al. (2006) found that the interannaul variability of this water vapor transport was one of the most key factors for differences in precipitation in southern China.

Based on these studies, we will analyze the dynamic and thermodynamic structure of China 2008 snowstorms. In particular, we will concentrate on investigating the characteristics of water vapor transport and variation. Using data from NIOST water vapor observational network, we try to examine whether the upstream moisture information provides a crucial precursor for winter precipitation in southeast China. For precipitation, we used surface precipitation observations from 2519 weather stations around China, provided by China Meteorological Administration (CMA). For other meteorological variables, we used U.S. National Center for Environmental Prediction-National Center for Atmospheric Research Reanalysis data (Kalnay et al. 1996), which provided geopotential height, meridional and zonal winds, humidity, and air temperature.

6.3. LARGE-SCALE CIRCULATION PATTERN, CONFLUENCE FRONTOGENESIS, AND TEMPERATURE INVERSION

Figure 40 shows a horizontal distribution of the first EOF (Empirical Orthogonal Function) and variation of its corresponding time coefficient of 500-hPa geopotential height in East Asian region during 0200UTC 10 January-2000UTC 2 February 2008. The EOF distribution reflects the primary atmospheric circulation patterns (the diviation contribution is 41.3%), which exhibited a pressure distribution of "south low-north high" during the snowstorm event. This result is consistent with "south trough-north ridge" anti-phased model for northern China winter storm in Wang and Xu (1979).

From the figure, one can also see that the time coefficient is positive during all four snowfall episodes (Figure 40b), especially presents a large value during the third episode. This suggests that the atmosphere circulation in the middle levels were dominated by the "south trough-north ridge" pattern throughout the entire snowstorms. This circulation pattern is in favor of convergence of cold-dry air from the north and warm-moist air from the south, and thusw promoting a frontogenesis in eastern China (the thick-black arrowed lines).

From the vertical-meridional cross section (Figure 41a and c), one can see that above the snowfall region at 925-700hPa levels, isotherms tilted to the north with increase of altitude. This indicates an existence of temperature inversion. From the vertical-zonal cross section (Figure 41b and d), a cold center was located in the region where heavy snowfall occurred.

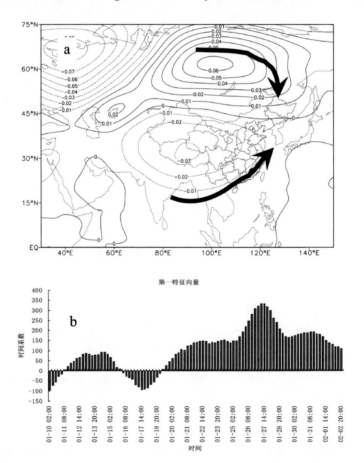

Figure 40. (a) The first EOF eigenvector for anomaly of NCEP-NCAR reanalysis geopotential height at 500hPa level, and (b) its time coefficient in the period of 10 January – 02 February 2008.

The cold-dry air intruded from north, acting as a "cold wedge" being pushed under lower-layers of atmosphere in southeastern China. Meanwhile, the warm-moist air transported from southwest was lifted when meeting with the cold air in the snowfall region. As a result, vertical wind shear was generated, which led to a vertical circulation and formed a "cold base" capped by a "warm lid above. This of course set up a very stable atmospheric structure, which was favorable for sustaining the storm.

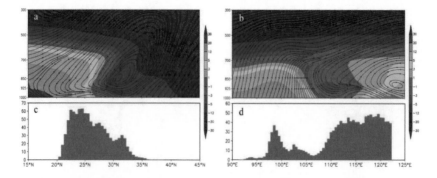

Figure 41. Averaged vertical circulations (arrow streamlines) and temperature (color-shaded, °C) a) in the north-south vertical cross-section along 110°-120°E; b) in the east-west vertical cross-section along 22.5°-32.5°N; c) and d) are corresponding total precipitation along these vertical sections (unit: mm).

6.4. LOW-LATITUDE WATER VAPOR SUPPLY AND TRANSPORT CHARACTERISTICS

Under the above large-scale circulation pattern of "south trough-north ridge," a key element triggering persistent snowfall is the continuous water vapor supply accompanied by the southwesterly flow in the low-latitude region. Figure 42 shows a horizontal distribution of averaged whole-column water vapor flux during the snowstorms. It is seen that there indeed existed a southwest channel of water vapor transport in south China. In order to verify that this southwesterly water vapor transport does contribute to the heavy snowfall in eastern China, we computed the correlation and lagged correlation between surface precipitation in the snowstorm region and meridional/zonal moisture fluxes (Figure 43). It is shown that the precipitation occurred during snowstorms are highly correlated with water vapor transports from Bay of the Bangle and South China Sea prior to the snowfall.

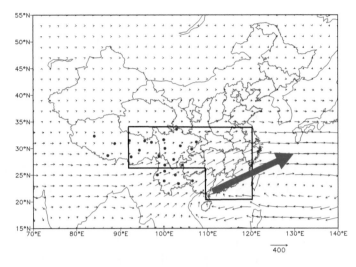

Figure 42. Averaged whole-column water vapor flux in the period of 10 January- 2 February 2008 (units: kg.m^{-1}.s^{-1}) and GPS stations of NIOST network (blue dots).

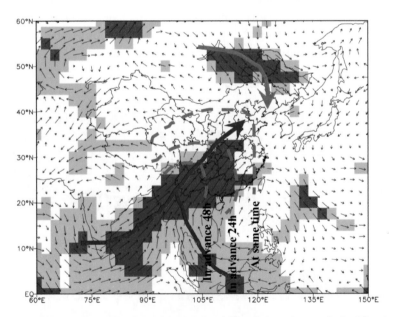

Figure 43. The correlation, 24-h, and 48-h lagged correlations (green dashed lines) vector of precipitation in southeast China during 10 January-2 February 2008 with whole-column water vapor flux (the regions with significant correlation components in both zonal and meridional are red shaded, while the regions with significant correlation component in either zonal or meridional are yellow shaded).

The two branches of moisture fluxes meet on the southeast side of the Tibetan Plateau and form a strong southwest water vapor channel (blue arrowed lines). This water vapor transport extends more to the northeast with time (green dashed lines), eventually providing moisture for the snowstorms. In addition, there is another branch of cold air coming down from Siberia and northern China (grey arrowed lines), which also contributes to the snowstorms.

6.5. WATER VAPOR SIGNAL IN THE UPSTREAM SENSITIVITY REGION FOR SNOWSTORMS

In recent years, global positioning system (GPS) becomes a new remote sensing technology for measuring atmospheric water content. Many studies shown that GPS measured total precipitable water can prove current weather forecasts (Gutman et al. 2004; Kuo 2006; Marcus et al. 2007). Several GPS stations within the NIOST observing network, discussed in the previous section, located along the pathway of the southwest transport of water vapor. Therefore, these GPS stations may provide valuable moisture information upstream of the snowstorms. Figure 44 plotted 6-hourly total precipitable water observed from seven stations in the NIOST network (station names are listed on the figure).

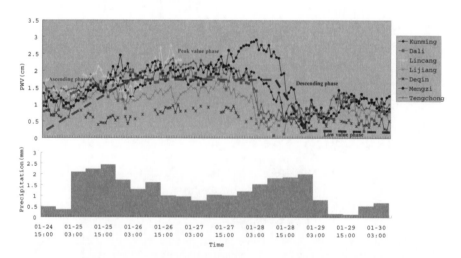

Figure 44. Hourly precipitable water vapor (PWV) observed from 7 GPS stations in the NIOST network during 24 January– 30 January 2008 (curve) and total precipitation in every 6 hours in the southern of China during the same time period (columns).

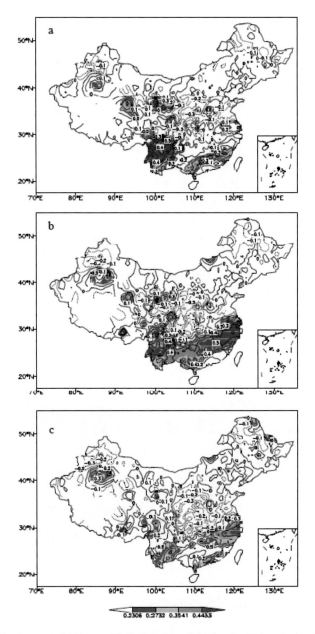

Figure 45. The lag correlation coefficients of precipitation in China during 10 January – 02 February 2008 with regional mean precipitable water vapor (PWV) from seven GPS stations in the NIOST observing network (a) at the same period, (b) in 24-h lag, and (c) in 48-h lag (the regions shaded by varied colors denote positive correlations at 0.10, 0.05, 0.01, and 0.001 significance level, respectively).

It is found that the time variation of upstream total precipitable water corresponds downstream storm precipitation quite well. Before a heavy snowfall, upstream precipitable water clearly presented an increasing trend. When the observed upstream precipitable water sustained a high value, downstream precipitation also experienced an increasing trend. This result suggests that the variation of total precipitable water in the upstream sensitive region may provide a predictor for downstream precipitation.

In order to examine the cause-and-effect relationship between upstream moisture and downstream precipitation, we computed the correlation, 24-h, and 48-h lagged correlations between these two fields (Figure 45). We found that the significantly positive region of the correlation was located in southwest China, near the water vapor transport source region, for the correlation of the two fields at the same time (no lag). With a 24-h time lag, the positive correlation region extended down to the Yangtze River basin, with a banded structure. Further increasing time lag to 48 hours, the correlation became to show a more teleconnection signature (in jumping signals).

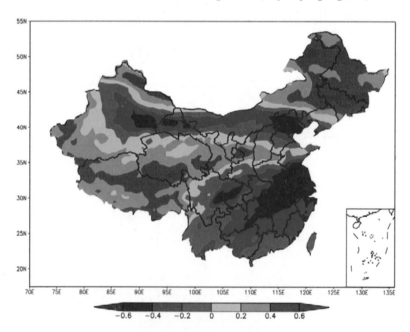

Figure 46. The 24-h lagged correlation coefficients of TBB during 24 January-30 January 2008 with regional mean precipitable water vapor (PWV) from seven GPS stations in the NIOST observing network.

Cloud black-body temperature (TBB) is often used to measure the convective activities. Generally speaking, the smaller the TBB, the more active the convection. In Figure 46, we plotted the 24-h lagged correlation between precipitable water vapor in the upstream region and TBB in the downstream region. It can be seen from the figure that the two fields showed a negative correlation in the southeastern China. That is, the larger the total precipitable water upstream, the stronger the convection downstream.

Through these statistical analyses, it is shown that water vapor transport in upstream sensitivity region provides a very good predictor for downstream precipitation. Therefore, NIOST observing and monitoring network can be used as an early warning system for downstream disastrous weather.

Chapter 8

THE WARNING AND PREDICTION OF DOWNSTREAM WEATHER BY ASSIMILATING PLATEAU OBSERVATIONAL DATA

The observations of surface temperature, moisture and other meteorological variables over the Tibetan Plateau areas can be very important and useful in the forecasting of precipitation in the downstream regions, including southeastern China and East Asia. During the past few years, the China-Japan joint project (JICA) has set up a new integrated observing network including GPS stations, PBL towers and AWS over the Tibetan Plateau and its surrounding areas (the southwestern regions of China), which may provide crucial information in the upstream sensitive regions for the severe weather occurring in the Yangtze-Huaihe Rivers basin. How to make use of these observations to improve the forecast of precipitation in the downstream regions poses a serious challenge for meteorologists.

With the development of remote sensing and high-speed computer technology as well as new data assimilation methods such as 3-dimensional or 4-dimensional variational data assimilation (3DVAR or 4DVAR) （Le Dimet and Talagrand 1986; Rabier and Anderson 1997; Courtier et al. 1994), Kalman Filter and Ensemble Kalman Filter (Miller 1986; Cohn and Parish 1991; Evens 2003), etc., data assimilation has become one of the most important aspects in weather forecasting during recent years.

Many studies have shown that data assimilation with advanced data assimilation methods is able to improve weather forecasts significantly (Zou and Xiao 1999; Peng and Zou 2003; Gu et al. 2005). However, it is still an unsolved issue on how to assimilate the observations (such as the AWS observations) from the observing network over the Tibetan Plateau and its surrounding areas into an advance mesoscale model, such as MM5 or WRF, to improve the downstream precipitation forecasting. As well known, the heavy winter snowstorms hitting most provinces of the middle and lower reaches of Yangtze River in January of 2008 caused severe damage of property. It is necessary and valuable to explore the effects of the assimilation of AWS observations over the Tibetan Plateau and its surrounding area in improving the forecasting of snowstorms occurring in the downstream regions of the plateau.

The data used in this study include surface temperature, moisture and pressure collected from the 24 AWS of the NIOST observing network over the Tibetan Plateau and its surrounding areas (Figure 47). The time interval of these observations used in this study is 1 hour. After performing a quality control of these observations, the data from 16 stations were used in each time level of the data assimilation. The quality control was done through the preprocessing of the WRF 3DVAR.

From Figure 47, one can see that most AWS whose data were used in the time level of 0000 UTC 25 January are located at the southeastern edge of the Tibetan Plateau, on the path of moisture transport from the Bay of Bengal to the Yangtze-Huaihe River basin. The top region of the Tibetan Plateau is located at the mid-troposphere with a mean surface pressure of about 500 hPa, and the slope is very steep over the southeastern edge of the plateau. Therefore, the AWS located at different height of the plateau slope may take a role analogous to some extent to that of radio soundings in obtaining the vertical "profile" information of the atmosphere (see Figure 48). On the other hand, the observations from radio soundings are usually available only twice a day, and may have large errors due to the problems of drifting with the air flow, non-synchronization at different height, and being subject to the local weather situation, while the observations of AWS at different height over the Tibetan Plateau are available every 30 minutes (or even at a higher sampling frequency) at fixing location/height under all weather situations, and synchronized at different height. Therefore, it is valuable to study the impacts of the assimilation of these AWS observations on improving the downstream weather prediction. Based on this thought, the following data assimilation experiments were designed and carried out.

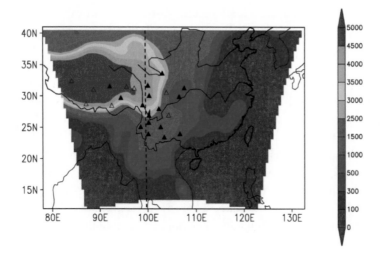

Figure 47. Model domain with terrain height (unit: m) and the locations of AWS stations. Solid triangles represent the stations whose observations are assimilated and empty triangles represent the ones which are lack of observations or discarded by quality control at the time level of 0000 UTC 25 January 2008.

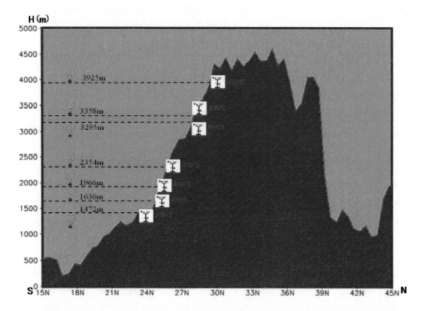

Figure 48. The height of the 7 AWS near longitude 99E (indicated by the dashed line in Figure 29) and the illustration of radio soundings at the corresponding height.

The model and the data assimilation scheme used in this study are the WRF model and its 3-dimensional variational (3DVAR) data assimilation system, respectively. The WRF model is a next-generation mesoscale numerical weather prediction system designed to serve both operational forecasting and atmospheric research needs (Michalakes et al. 1998). The WRF-3DVAR system was developed from MM5 3DVAR system by the National Center for Atmospheric Research (NCAR), U.S. (Barker et al. 2004). Considering the advantage of higher sampling frequency of the AWS observations, a multi-cycle 3DVAR scheme was employed in this study. The heavy snowstorm occurred during 25-28 January 2008 was selected for this study, which hit most provinces in south China and caused huge damage of property and loss of lives. The setup of model domain for numerical experiments is shown in Figure 29. The horizontal resolution is 120 km with 27 sigma levels.

The following experiments are performed. CNTR: control run without data assimilation; DA-1: data assimilation experiment with only one-cycle 3DVAR applying at 0000 UTC 25 January 2008; and DA-2: data assimilation experiment with multi-cycle 3DVAR applying every hour from 1800 UTC 24 August to 0000 UTC 25 January 2008.

The original initial conditions (IC) and boundary conditions (BC) were obtained from NCEP final analysis with $1° \times 1°$ resolution. Figure 49 shows the increments of sea level pressure, temperature, and moisture flux near surface (at the 2nd sigma level) for IC after data assimilation (DA-2). Large decrease of seal level pressure are found over the Tibetan Plateau and its eastern regions, which indicates that the vortexes with low surface pressure over these regions were intensified after the assimilation of AWS data. The increments of moisture flux indicate that the moisture transportation from the Bay of Bengal and the moisture convergence over the southeastern regions of the Tibetan Plateau were intensified after data assimilation. Significant positive increments of temperature are also seen over the downstream regions of the plateau.

Figure 50 presents the increments of geopotential height and v-component of winds at 500 hPa (the approximate mean value of the surface pressure over the top region of the Tibetan Plateau) for IC after data assimilation (DA-2). Large decrease of height is found over the plateau and its eastern areas, resulting in a stronger southern wind over the eastern regions of the Tibetan Plateau, which is beneficial to the moisture transport. Therefore, the assimilation of the observations from the AWS over the large-scale steep slope of the plateau is able to improve the objective description of the atmospheric structure over the upstream areas, i.e., the Tibetan Plateau and its surrounding areas.

Now let us see whether the above adjustments for IC after data assimilation result in an improvement of the simulation of snowstorms. All of the experiments performed the simulation of precipitation for the same period of 0000 UTC 25—0000 UTC 28 January 2008 using the original IC/BC (CNTR) or "optimal" IC/BC after data assimilation (DA-1 and DA-2). The results show that the two data assimilation experiments (DA-1 and DA-2) improved the simulation of precipitation up to a period of 48 hours, with the improvements being more significant in the second 24-h period. To save space, here only the precipitation of the second 24-h period ending at 0000 UTC 27 January is presented (Figure 51). From Figure 51, one can also find that DA-2 outperformed DA-1 significantly. Particularly, the observed heavy rain center over the region of (25-27°N, 115-120°E) was well simulated in DA-2 and the false rainfall in the southwestern regions of China in CNTR was reduced greatly in DA-2.

Significant improvements were also obtained when the AWS data over Tibetan Plateau and its surrounding areas were assimilated into WRF 3DVAR for the simulation of another heavy snowstorm occurring at the lower reach of Yangtze River during 17-20 January 2008. Therefore, the AWS data over the Tibetan Plateau and its surrounding areas could be very useful in the forecasting of precipitation occurred in the downstream regions of the plateau.

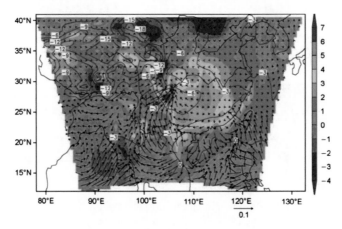

Figure 49. The increments of sea level pressure (blue solid lines, unit: hPa), and temperature (shaded, unit: ℃) and moisture flux (vector, unit: kg m kg−1 s−1) near surface (at the 2nd sigma level) at 0000 UTC 25 January 2008 after data assimilation (DA-2).

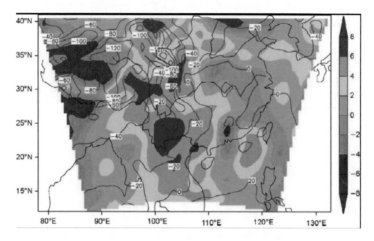

Figure 50. The increments of geopotential height (blue solid lines, unit: m) and v-component of wind (shaded, unit: m s−1) at 500 hPa at 0000 UTC 25 January 2008 after data assimilation (DA-2).

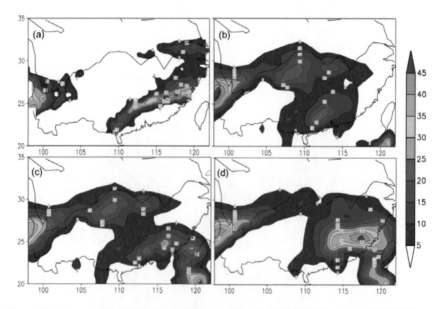

Figure 51. Accumulated 24-h precipitation ending at 0000 UTC January 27 2008 for observations (a); CNTR (b); DA-1 (c); and DA-2 (d) (unit: mm).

The numerical experiments in this study reveal that the assimilation of the observations from the AWS over the larges-scale slope on the southeastern edge of the plateau is able to adjust the 3-dimensional structure of the atmospheric thermal-dynamics, and thus help to reveal the early-warning "strong signals" in the upstream sensitive area for the weather system occurring in the east of the plateau. Furthermore, the AWS over the large-scale slope of the plateau have advantages over the normal radio soundings in the aspects of sampling frequency, location/height fixing, and synchronization.

Chapter 9

EFFECT OF TOPOGRAPHY OVER THE TIBETAN PLATEAU ON SUMMER PRECIPITATION IN CHINA

The dynamical and thermal forcing of the Tibetan Plateau plays important roles in not only the formation of the monsoon circulation but also the development of weather systems over East China in summer (Tao and Ding 1981; Yanai et al. 1992; Wu and Zhang 1998; Tao et al. 1998; Xu et al. 2001). For example, Xu et al. (2001) and Wang et al. (2003) found that cloud systems developed over the Tibetan Plateau could further intensify to form deep and matured super convective cloud clusters when they propagate eastward, contributing to the summer monsoon precipitation in China. They suggested that the Tibetan Plateau be an important source of convective cloud systems to the development of floods in East China, especially, in the middle and lower reaches of Yangtze River Basin (YRB).

Despite considerable progress has been made in understanding the impacts of the Tibetan Plateau on the East Asian climate, current state-of-the-art global general circulation models (GCMs) with coarse/moderate horizontal resolutions are still poor in simulating the mean and seasonal cycle of precipitation in the East Asian monsoon region (Lau 1992, Kang et al. 2002). Regional high-resolution models start to show consistent improvements in simulating the regional climate in East Asia (e.g., Wang et al. 2003, Wang et al. 2004). It is, however, unclear whether the improved simulations by regional models are because of the use of more advanced model physics or higher horizontal model resolution or both. Since high resolution models can better resolve the mesoscale feature in topography over the Tibetan Plateau, we hypothesize that the resolution of the model topography over the Tibetan Plateau contributes significantly to the improved simulations of the East Asia climate by regional high resolution models. We will demonstrate that the mesoscale topography over the Tibetan Plateau plays important roles in generating/enhancing mesoscale disturbances, increasing the surface heat flux, and triggering convective cloud systems over the Tibetan Plateau in summer. They generally propagate eastward and enhance the downstream precipitation systems in the YRB in China.

9.1. MODEL AND EXPERIMENTAL DESIGN

The model used in this study is the community regional climate model, RegCM3, which is described in detail in Pal et al. (2007). RegCM3 is a limited area, hydrostatic, primitive equation model with sigma as the vertical coordinate. The Grell scheme with Fritsch and Chappell closure is used for deep convection parameterization (Grell, 1993). The radiation is adopted from the Community Climate Model version 3 (CCM3, Kiehl et al. 1998). The sub-grid vertical mixing is parameterized with the non-local scheme of Holtslag and Boville (1993). The Biosphere-Atmosphere Transfer Scheme (BATS) of Dickinson et al. (1993) is used for the land surface processes.

The RegCM3 was run with 18 vertical levels and at 30 km grid spacing with a domain size of 180 by 120 grid points centered at 30.5°N, 100°E. The model domain covers the shaded areas in Figure 52, including the Tibetan Plateau and the surrounding areas in East Asia. In the standard settings, the model was initialized at 0012 UTC on 9 June 1998 and integrated through 31 July. The National Centers for Environmental Prediction/National Center for Atmospheric Research (NCEP/NCAR) reanalysis at every 6-h interval was used as both the initial and lateral boundary conditions for RegCM3. The summer of 1998 was chosen because of the record heavy rainfall that caused severe floods in the YRB since 1954. The detailed description of the summer rainfall and its evolution can be found in Ding and Hu (2003) and Wang et al. (2003).

Two ensemble simulations were carried out, each including five members with initial conditions spanning 5 days, centered on 9 June 1998. In the control simulation (CNTRL), the horizontal resolution of 30 km was used for both the model grids and the topography (Figure 52a). In the sensitivity simulation (SENTR), the model was run at 30 km horizontal resolution but the 120 km resolution topography over the Tibetan Plateau was used. Namely, the 120 km resolution topography was interpolated to the 30 km model grids in SENTR to replace the 30 km resolution topography used in CNTRL for the regions where the topography is higher than 2,000 m and south of 40°N in the model domain only over the Tibetan Plateau (Figure 52b). As we can see from Figure 52, there are significant differences in model topography over the Tibetan Plateau between the CNTRL and SENTR simulations.

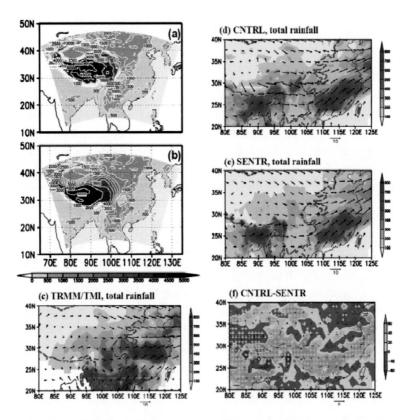

Figure 52. The model domain (sector areas) and orography in (a) control experiment (CNTRL) and (b) sensitivity experiment with coarse resolution orography over the Tibetan Plateau (SENTR). Contours show the orography with contour interval of 500m. Spatial distributions of total rainfall (shaded, units: mm) and 500 hPa wind (vectors, units: m/s) during June 12-July 31 1998 from (c) observations, (d) control experiment, and (e) sensitivity experiment with coarse resolution orography over the Tibetan Plateau. (f) shows the difference (CNTRL-SENTR) fields in total rainfall and 700 hPa winds between the control and sensitivity experiment. The thick dashed curve denotes the contour with 1000m-topography in (c)-(e). The symbols "+" in (f) indicate areas with statistically significance at 90% confidence level.

The mesoscale feature in model topography over the Tibetan Plateau in CNTRL was smoothed out in SENTR. Therefore, the difference between the CNTRL and SENTR simulations can be considered as a result of the effect of mesoscale topography over the Tibetan Plateau. The results discussed below are the ensemble mean for each of the simulations.

9.2. RESULTS

Figures 52c-f show the total precipitation and the mean wind vectors at 500 hPa during June 12-July 31, 2008 from the observation, CNTRL, and SENTR ensemble means, respectively, and the differences between the CNTRL and SENTR (CNTRL minus SENTR) in which regions with statistical significance above 90% confidence levels were marked with "+". The observed total rainfall was obtained based on 656 station data over China in 1998. As done in Wang et al. (2003) and Sen et al. (2004), the station daily rainfall data were first objectively interpolated onto the model grids using the Cressman interpolation method.

The observed heavy rainfall occurred along the YRB (26-32°N), South China, and Indochina Peninsula (Figure 52c). Except for a slightly southeastward shift of the heavy rainfall area in the YRB and a significant underestimation of rainfall over South China and the Indochina Peninsula, the control simulation reproduced the rainfall distribution and low-level circulation downstream of the Tibetan Plateau reasonably well (Figure 52d). To have a quantitative assessment for the overall performance of the control simulation in the region downstream of the Tibetan Plateau, statistics similar to those in Wang et al. (2003) were conducted for the simulated precipitation in the area of 25°-35°N, 110°-120°E (Table 1).

The model estimated mean daily rainfall in the control simulation is slightly higher than the observed (10.5 versus 9.7 mm d^{-1}). Spatial and temporal correlation coefficients are high at 49% and 72% (with confidence level above 95%), respectively, indicating that the model not only reproduced the spatial pattern reasonably but also captured well the temporal evolution of precipitation events in the region. We can thus consider that the control simulation reproduced reasonably well the precipitation downstream of the Tibetan Plateau and the results can be compared with those from the sensitivity simulation to understand how the mesoscale topography over the Tibetan Plateau affects the downstream precipitation in the middle and lower reaches of the YRB.

Table 1. Statistics of the model simulated precipitation in the area of 25°-35°N, 110°-120°E for the control and the sensitivity experiments [a], respectively

	Mean Rainfall (mm)	Spatial Correlation	Temporal Correlation	Bias
OBS [b]	9.70			
CNTRL	10.49	0.49	0.72	0.79
SENTR	8.78	0.39	0.58	0.92

[a] Precipitation in mm.d^{-1}; CNTRL, control; SENTR, sensitivity.
[b] OBS, observed.

In the SENTR simulation with the coarse resolution topography over the Tibetan Plateau, the rainfall amount was considerably reduced in most areas of the model domain, especially over the eastern Tibetan Plateau and the YRB (Figure 52e). Except for a significant reduction of rainfall over the western Tibetan Plateau and northeast China, rainfall over the eastern part and downstream of the Tibetan Plateau was significantly increased due to the presence of the mesoscale topography over the Tibetan Plateau (Figure 52f) in the CNTRL simulation. In addition, the southwesterly monsoon flow was also stronger over the central and east China in the CNTRL simulation than in the SENTR. The area averaged daily mean rainfall during the whole simulation period in the middle and lower reaches of the YRB in the SENTR was considerably lower than in the CNTRL (Table 1). The mean rainfall rate was reduced by 16.3% in SENTR compared to the CNTRL. Compared with observations, although the CNTRL simulation slightly overestimated the mean precipitation, the SENTR simulation considerably underestimated the mean precipitation. Both spatial and temporal correlation coefficients with the observation in SENTR were considerably lower than in the CNTRL (Table 1), indicating the overall degraded performance of the model with coarse resolution topography in the SENTR.

The above results demonstrate that high model resolution to resolve the mesoscale topography over the Tibetan Plateau is very important for the realistic simulation of precipitation in East Asia. To understand how the mesoscale feature in topography over the Tibetan Plateau affects the downstream precipitation in the YRB, we have examined the difference in the high-frequency synoptic and sub-synoptic scale activities in the two simulations. Ding and Liu (2001) showed the contribution by the eastward propagating mesoscale and sub-synoptic disturbances initiated over the Tibetan Plateau to the 1998 summer precipitation over the YRB. As we can see from the temporal evolution of the cloud top temperature (TBB, blackbody temperature) averaged in the latitude band between 25°N based on 6 hourly satellite observations (Figure 53a), the convective cloud clusters originated over the Tibetan Plateau moved eastward to enhance the rainstorms in middle and lower reaches of the YRB. Figures 53b and 53c show the vertical cyclonic relative vorticity (only positive values included in the average) at 500 hPa averaged in the same latitude band from the CNTRL and SENTR simulations, respectively. The positive relative vorticity in the lower troposphere generally corresponds to cyclonic circulation and low pressure systems. The positive relative vorticity and eastward propagation signal were clearly seen in the CNTRL simulation (Figure 53b). They, however, were much weaker in SENTR (Figure 53c) both over the Tibetan Plateau and downstream in YRB. This suggests that the cyclonic disturbances and low pressure systems were suppressed in the SENTR due to the lack of mesoscale topographic triggering over the Tibetan Plateau compared to those in the CNTRL.

The activities of high frequency mesoscale and sub-synoptic disturbances can be measured by the eddy kinetic energy (EKE) in the simulations. The EKE is defined as

$$EKE = \frac{1}{2}\left[(u - \overline{u})^2 + (v - \overline{v})^2\right]$$

where u, v are zonal and meridional wind components at 500 hPa, $\overline{u}$, $\overline{v}$ are their time mean during June 12-July 31, 2008. Figure 54 shows the time-mean EKE during the simulation period from NCEP reanalysis, the CNTRL, and the SENTR simulations, respectively. Because of the relative coarse resolution, NCEP reanalysis largely underestimated the EKE (Figure 54a). In the CNTRL simulation, there was a zonally elongated high EKE band between 30°-36°N over the Tibetan Plateau and extended eastward to the YRB and southwest China (Figure 54b), indicating active high-frequency mesoscale and sub-synoptic disturbances during the simulation period. In contrast, although a similar high EKE band appeared in the SENTR simulation (Fig 54c), the absolute values are much smaller, indicating a suppression of the mesoscale and sub-synoptic activities. Comparing Figs. 54 with Figure 52, one can see that the high EKE band is collocated with the high topography with considerably mesoscale variability over the Tibetan Plateau in the CNTRL simulation. This indicates that mesoscale topography over the Tibetan Plateau contributed significantly to the generation of high-frequency mesoscale and sub-synoptic disturbances over the Tibetan Plateau. These disturbances on one hand produced precipitation over the Tibetan Plateau, and on the other hand enhanced the precipitation systems over the YRB when they propagated downstream to East China.

The high frequency, mesoscale and sub-synoptic disturbances may also enhance the surface heat flux due to the increased near surface wind speed. As shown in Figure 54, the total time-mean surface (sensible and latent) heat flux was generally larger in the CNTRL than in the SENTR, especially over the central and southern Tibetan Plateau and in the middle and lower reaches of the YRB (Figure 54d). The increased surface sensible heat flux (Figure 54e) dominates the enhanced total surface heat flux, especially over the Tibetan Plateau (Figure 54d). The changes in surface latent heat flux over the Tibetan Plateau were generally small except for the negative areas west of the 90°E over the Tibetan Plateau and positive areas along the south flank of the Tibetan Plateau (Figure 54f).

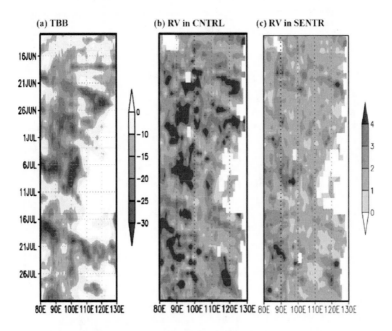

Figure 53. Time-longitude section of cloud top temperature TBB (unit: °C) averaged between 25°-35°N from Satellite observation (a), and cyclonic relative vorticity (units: 10^{-5} s^{-1}) averaged between 25°-35°N at 700 hPa from the control experiment (b) and the sensitivity experiment (c) during June 12-July 31, 1998.

The larger latent heat flux over the western Tibetan Plateau was consistent with the increased precipitation in the SENTR (Figure 52f). Overall, the presence of mesoscale topography over the Tibetan Plateau in the CNTRL enhanced the high-frequency disturbances and increased the surface heat flux over the Tibetan Plateau. These may enhance the convective systems both over the Tibetan Plateau and downstream over the YRB in China. This could explain why the precipitation over the middle-lower reaches of the YRB was increased in the CNTRL.

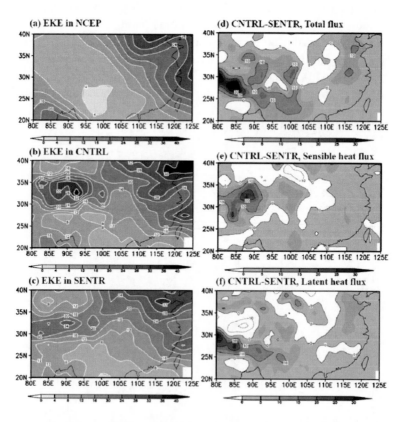

Figure 54. Left: Spatial distributions of eddy kinetic energy (EKE, m^2 s^{-2}) at 500 hPa averaged during June 12-July 31, 1998 from (a) NCEP reanalysis, (b) control experiment, and (c) sensitivity experiment with coarse resolution topography over the Tibetan Plateau. Right: Differences (W m^{-2}) in (d) total surface (sensible + latent heat) fluxes, (e) sensible heat flux, and (f) latent heat flux between the control and sensitivity experiments averaged during June 12-July 31, 1998.

9.3. SUMMARY

Previous observational and modeling studies have demonstrated that both thermal and mechanical effects of the Tibetan Plateau play important roles in the onset and evolution of Asian and East Asian monsoon and the moisture transport and precipitation in summer in China. Observational studies have also shown that mesoscale convective cloud systems that are initiated over the Tibetan Plateau and propagate eastward may contribute significantly to downstream precipitation over the YRB in China. The heterogeneous sensible heat flux over the Tibetan Plateau is proposed as a triggering mechanism for the convective cloud systems (Tao and Ding 1981). In this study, results from the regional climate model simulations demonstrate that mesoscale feature of topography over the Tibetan Plateau plays an important role in triggering and enhancing the activities of mesoscale and sub-synoptic disturbances over the Tibetan Plateau. These disturbances increase the surface heat flux over the Tibetan Plateau and propagate eastward and enhance the downstream summer convective systems and precipitation over the middle-lower reaches of the YRB in China. Since this study only performed one summer simulations, the robustness of the finding yet to be confirmed with multi-year simulations in the future. In a study by Xie et al. (2006) demonstrated that the coastal mesoscale mountains in South Asia play critical roles in organizing monsoon convection and large-scale monsoon circulation in summer in Asia and East Asia. The results from this study strongly suggest the need of high-resolution model to better resolve the topography not only in coastal South Asia but also over the Tibetan Plateau for the realistic simulations of the East Asian summer climate.

Chapter 10

POSTSCRIPT AND CONCLUDING REMARKS

In this study, we have analyzed the impact of the Tibetan Plateau on the regional climate and disastrous weather in China and Asia. In particular, we examined the Tibetan Plateau's roles in initiating convective clouds, transporting these convective systems downstream, attracting moisture from low-latitude oceans and re-channeling the moisture to eastern China and East Asia, and causing flood/drought conditions in association with Asian summer monsoon. These analyses led to applications and operation of monitoring and warning systems over the upstream sensitive area, thus increased human's capability to mitigate the impact of natural disasters.

Due to its high-rise land surface with strong radiative forcing, the Tibetan Plateau is a favorable place to generate a lot of convective cloud clusters. When these mesoscale convective systems move downslope into eastern China lowlands, these systems are typically intensified with lee-cyclonic forcing and developed into large-scale weather systems. In addition, because of its unique geographic land feature and location, the Tibetan Plateau plays a crucial role in Asian summer monsoon. As a large-scale heat source, the Tibetan Plateau not only attracts warm-moist air from low-latitude oceans, it also re-channels this moisture eastward. The downstream transport of water vapor has a profound implication for storm development and reinforcement, as well as for the flood/drought conditions in eastern China and East Asia in general.

Based on these understandings, a new integrated observational system over the Tibetan Plateau has been designed and implemented since 2005. The goal of this observing network is to monitoring any development of weather disturbances in the upstream sensitive regions. Such observations may provide us with crucial information to make an early warning for disastrous weather events potential threat to downstream regions.

We carried out two applications of this monitoring system. In one case, we used water vapor observations obtained on the southeast side of the plateau to find statistical correlations of downstream precipitation in China 2008 grand-scale snowstorms. We found that the upstream moisture information may provide an important predictor for downstream heavy precipitation events. In the second case, we actually experimented with assimilation of surface weather observations into an atmospheric forecast model. With these data ingested, significant improvement of downstream weather forecasts can be obtained.

REFERENCES

Ashfaq, M., Y. Shi, W. Tung, R. J. Trapp, X. Gao, J. S. Pal, and N. S. Diffenbaugh, Suppression of south Asian summer monsoon precipitation in the 21st century. *Geophys. Res. Lett.,* 36, L01704, doi:10.1029/2008GL036500, (2009).

Bai, J., and X., Xu. Atmospheric hydrological budget with its effects over Tibetan Plateau. Journal of Geographical Sciences, 14, 81-86, (2004).

Bansod, S. D., Z. Yin, Z. Lin, X. Zhang, Thermal field over Tibetan Plateau and Indian summer monsoon rainfall. *Int. J. Climatol.,* 23, 1589-1605, (2003).

Barker, D. M, Huang W, Guo Y R, et al. A three-dimensional (3DVAR) data assimilation system for use with MM5: Implementation and initial results. *Mon. Wea. Rev.,* 2004, 132, 897-914.

Chen L. X, Zhu, Q., Ou, H. et al. East Asian Monsoon, Beijing, China *Meteorological Press*, 1991, 49-61.

Chen, L. X, Reiter, E R, Feng, Z Q. The atmospheric heat source over the Tibetan Plateau: May-August 1979. *Mon. Wea. Rev.,* 1985, 113: 1771-1790.

Chen, T. C., Yen M. C. The water vapor transport associated with the 30–50 day oscillation over the Asian monsoon regions during 1979 summer. *Mon. Wea. Rev.,* 1988, 116, 1983 – 2002.

Cohn S. E., Parish D. F. The behavior of forecast error covariances for a Kalman filter in two dimensions. *Mon. Wea. Rev.,* 1991, 119, 1757-1785.

Courtier, P., Thepaut, J. N., Hollingsworth, A. A strategy for operational implementation of 4D-Var using an incremental approach. *Quart. J. Roy. Meteor. Soc.,* 1994, 120, 1367-1388.

Dai, J. X. Tibetan Plateau Climate (in Chinese), Beijing, China, *Meteorology Press*, 1990, 368pp.

Davis, M. E., Thompson, L. G., Yao, T., Wang, N. Forcing of the Asian monsoon on the Tibetan Plateau: Evidence from high-resolution ice core and tropical coral record. *J. Geophys. Res.,* 110, D0410, (2005).

Deng, Y. P, Cheng, L. S, Zhang, X. L. Three-phase cloud explicity precipitation scheme and mesoscale numerical simulation for generated cause of the "96.1" snowstorm. *Plateau Meteor* (in Chinese), 2000, 19 (4): 401-414.

Dickinson, R.E., A. Henderson-Sellors, and P.J. Kennedy, 1993: Biosphere-Atmosphere Transfer Scheme (BATS) version 1e as coupled to the NCAR Community Climate Model, *NCAR Technical Note*, NCAR/TN-387+STR, NCAR, Boulder, CO, 72pp.

Ding Y H and C L Chan (2005), The East Asian summer monsoon: an overview. *Meteor. Atmos. Phys.*, 89, 117-142.

Ding Y. (1994), *Monsoons over China*, Kluwer Academic Publisher, Dordrecht/Boston/London, 419 pp.

Ding Y., (1992), Effects of the Qinghai-Xizang (Tibetan) Plateau on the Circulation Features over the Plateau and Its Surrounding Areas. *Adv. Atmos. Sci.*, 9(1), 112-130.

Ding, Y. The outlook of environmental changes in western China. Assessment of Environment Evolution of Western China. Science Press (in Chinese), Beijing, China. 2, 147-170, (2002).

Ding, Y.-H, and Y. Liu, 2001: Onset and the evolution of the summer monsoon over the South China Sea during SCSMEX Field Experiment I 1998. *J. Meteor. Soc. Japan*, 79, 255-276.

Ding, Y., Y. Liu, Y. Sun, and Y. Song, Weakening of the Asian Summer Monsoon and Its Impact on the Precipitation Pattern in China. *International Journal of Water Resources Development,* 26, 423-439, (2010).

Duan, K., Yao, T., Thompson, L. G. Response of monsoon precipitation in the Himalayas to global warming. J. Geophys. Res., 111, D19110, (2006).

Evens, G. The Ensemble Kalman Filter: Theoretical formulation and practical implementation. *Ocean Dyn.*, 2003, 53, 343-367.

Flohn, H., 1957: Large-scale aspects of the "summer monsoon" in South and East Asia. *J. Meteor. Soc. Japan*, 75, 180–186.

Flohn, H., Contribution to a meteorology of the Tibetan Highlands, *Atmos. Sci. Paper*, Colorado State University, Fort Collins, 1968, 130, 120pp.

Ge, Q., X. Guo, and J. Zheng (2008), Meiyu in the middle and lower reaches of the Yangtze River since 1736, *Chinese Science Bulletin*, 53 (1), 107-114.

Gong, D, J, Li, Z. J. Low-level jet and heavy snow or snowstorm in Inner Mongolia. *Meteor. Mon.* (in Chinese), 2001, 27 (12): 3-7.

Grell, G..A., 1993: Prognostic evaluation of assumptions used by cumulus parameterization, *Mon. Wea. Rev.*, 121, 764-787.

Gu, J, Xiao, Q, Kuo, Y. H, et al. Assimilation and simulation of Typhoon Rusa (2002) using the WRF system. *Adv. Atmos. Sci*, 2005, 22(3): 415-427.

Gutman, S. I, Sahm, S. R, Benjamin, S. G, et al. Rapid retrieval and assimilation of ground based GPS precipitable water observations at the NOAA forecast systems laboratory: Impact on weather forecasts. *J. Meteor. Soc. Japan*, 2004, 82: 351 – 360.

Hahn, G.., S. Manabe, 1975: The role of mountains in the South Asian monsoon circulation. *J. Atmos. Sci.*, 77, 1515-1541.

He, H.-Y., J.W. McGinnis, Z. Song, and M. Yanai, 1987: Onset of the Asian summer monsoon in 1979 and the effect of the Tibetan Plateau. *Mon. Wea. Rev.*, 115, 1966-1995.

He, X. C, Ding, Y. H, He, J. H, et al. An analysis on anomalous precipitation in southern China during winter monsoons. *Acta. Meteor. Sinica* (in Chinese), 2006, 64 (5): 594-604.

Holtslag, A.A.M., and B.A. Boville, 1993: Local versus nonlocal boundary-layer diffusion in a global climate model. *J. Climate*, 6, 1825-1842.

Hu, G, Ding, Y. A study on the energy and water cycle over Changjiang-Huaihe river basins 1991 heavy rain periods. *Acta Meteor Sinica*, 2003, 61(2): 146-163.

Huang, R. et al. Studies on the relationship between the severe climate disasters in China and the East Asia climate system. *Chinese Journal of Atmos. Sci. (in Chinese)*, 27 (4): 770 – 787, (2003).

Huang, R. H, Zhang, Z. Z, Huang, G, et al. Characteristics of the water vapor transport in East Asian monsoon region and its difference from that in South Asian monsoon region in summer. *Chinese J. Atmos. Sci.* (in Chinese), 1998, 22 (4): 460 –469.

Huang, R.-H., 1985: Numerical simulation of three-dimensional teleconnections in the summer circulation over the northern hemisphere. *Adv. Atmos. Sci.*, 2, 81-92.

Ji, G. L, Yao, L. C, Yuan, F. M, et al. Characteristics of surface and atmospheric heating fields over Qinghai-Xizang Plateau during the winter in 1982. *Sci. China Ser. B*, 1986, 29(8): 876-888.

Kalnay, E., M. Kanamitsu, R. Kistler, and Coauthors, 1996: The NCEP/NCAR 40-year reanalysis project. *Bull. Amer. Meteor. Soc.*, 77, 437–471.

Kang, I.-S., and coauthors, 2002: Intercomparison of the climatological variations of Asian summer monsoon precipitation simulated by 10 GCMs. *Climate Dyn.*, 19, 383-395.

Kato, K., 1989: Seasonal transition of the lower-level circulation systems around the Baiu front in China in 1979 and its relation to the Northern Summer Monsoon. *J. Meteor. Soc. Japan*, 67, 249-265.

Kiehl, J.T., J.J. Hack, G..B. Bonan, B.A. Boville, D.L. Williamson, and P.J. Rasch, 1998: The National Climate Center for Atmospheric Research Community Climate Model (CCM3). *J. Climate*, 11, 1307-1326.

Kuo, Y. Assimilation of ground-based GPS data for short-range precipitation forecast. *Preprints, Fourth Korea–US Joint Workshop on Mesoscale Observations, Data Assimilation, and Modeling for Severe Weather*, 2006, Seoul, Korea, KOSEF and NSF/OISE, 38 – 41.

Lau, K.-M., 1992: East Asian summer monsoon rainfall variability and climate teleconnection. *J. Meteor. Soc. Japan*, 70, 211-242.

Le Dimet, F. X., Talagrand, O. Variational algorithms for analysis and assimilation of meteorological observations: theoretical aspects. *Tellus*, 1986, 38A: 97-110.

Li, H., A. Dai, T. Zhou, and J. Lu, Responses of East Asian summer monsoon to historical SSTand atmospheric forcing during 1950–2000. *Clim. Dyn.*, doi:10.1007/s00382-008-0482-7, (2008).

Liu, G. W. Atmospheric Processes of Water Cycle (in Chinese), Beijing, China, *Science Press*, 1997.

Liu, X., and Z. Yin, 2001: Spatial and temporal variation of summer precipitation over the eastern Tibetan Plateau and the North Atlantic Oscillation. *J. Climate*, 14, 2896-2909.

Liu, X., Chen, B. Climate warming in the Tibetan Plateau during recent decades. Int. J. Climat., 20, 1729-1742, (2000).

Lu, C., Yu, G., Xie, G. Tibetan Plateau serves as a water tower. Geoscience and Remote Sensing Symposium, IEEE International, 5, 3120-3123, (2005).

Lu, L., Zhou G., Direct solar radiation and total radiation in the Mt. Qomolangma area in 1992, *J. Solar Energy* (in Chinese), 1995, 16(3): 229-232.

Lu, R., and B. Dong, Response of the Asian Summer Monsoon to Weakening of Atlantic Thermohaline Circulation. *Adv. Atmos. Sci.*, 25, 723-736, (2008).

Lu, Y. R, Gao, G. D. The mean transfer of water –vapour in the atmosphere over China. *Plateau Meteor.* (in Chinese), 1983, 2 (4): 34-38.

Luo, H., The effect of sensible heat transfer on the Tibetan Plateau on the formation of Asia monsoon circulation, Meteorological Science and Technology (10) (in Chinese), Beijing, China, *Meteorology Press*, 1987, 89-102.

Ma, Y., and Coauthors, Roof of the world: Tibetan observation and research platform. *Bull. Amer. Meteor. Soc.*, 89, 1487-1492.

Maddox, R. A. Mesoscale convective complex. *Bull. Amer. Meteor. Sci.*, 1980, 61, 1374-1387.

Manabe, S. and T.B. Terpstra, 1974: The effects of mountains on the general circulation of the atmosphere as identified by numerical experiments, *J. Atmos. Sci.*, 31, 3–42.

Marcus, S, Kim, J, Chin, T, et al. 2007. Influence of GPS precipitable water vapor retrievals on quantitative precipitation forecasting in Southern California. *J. Appl. Meteor. and Clim.*, 2007, 46, 1828 – 1839.

Michalakes, J, Dudhia, J, Gill, D, et al. Design of a next-generation regional weather research and forecast model: Towards Teracomputing. New Jersey, *World Scientific*, River Edge, 1998. 117-124.

Miller, R. N. Toward the application of the Kalman Filter to regional open ocean modeling. *J. Phys. Oceanogr.*, 1986, 16, 72-86.

Murakami, T., and W.G. Huang, 1984 : Orographic effect of the Tibetan Plateau on the rainfall variations over Central China during the 1979 summer. *J. Meteor. Soc. Japan*, 62, 895-909.

New, M., Lister, D., Hulme, M., et al. A high-resolution data set of surface climate over global land areas. *Climate Res.* 2002; 21: 1 – 25.

Ninomiya, K., and H. Muraki. 1986: Large-Scale Circulations over East Asia during Baiu Period. *J. Meteorol. Soc. Japan*, 64(3), 409-429.

Nitta, T., Observational study of heat sources over the eastern Tibetan Plateau during summer monsoon season. *J. Meteor. Soc. Japan*, 1983, 61, 590–605.

Oku, Y., H. Ishikawa, S. Haginoya, and Y. Ma, Recent trends in land surface temperature on the Tibetan Plateau. *J. Climate*, 15, 2995-3003, (2006).

Pal, J.S., and coauthors, 2007: RegCM3 and RegCNET: Regional climate modeling for the developing world. *Bull. Amer. Meteor. Soc.*, 88, 1395-1409.

Pearce, F. Flooded out. New Scientist, 2189, 18, (1999).

Peng, S. Q, Zou, X. Assimilation of ground-based GPS zenith total delay and rain gauge precipitation observations using 4D-Var and their impact on short-range QPF. *J. Met. Soc. of Japan*, 2003, 82, 491-506.

Qian, J., W. Tao, and K.-M. Lau, 2004: Mechanisms for torrential rain associated with the Mei-yu development during SCSMEX 1998. *Mon. Wea. Rev.*, 132, 3-27.

Rabier, F, Anderson, E. The ECMWF implementation of three dimensional variational (3DVar) data assimilation Part II: Structure function. *Quart. J. Roy. Meteor. Soc.*, 1997, 123, 27-52.

Ren, R. C., Y. M. Liu, and G. X. Wu, 2004: On the Short-term variation of subtropical anticyclone over the western Pacific affected by the mid-high latitudes circulation in July 1998. *Chinese Journal of Atmospheric Sciences*, 28, 571-578.

Sen, O. L., Y. Wang, and B. Wang, 2004: Impact of Indochina deforestation on the East Asian summer monsoon. *J. Climate*, 17, 1366-1380.

Tao, S. Y, Chen, L. S, Xu, X., et al. The Second Tibetan Plateau Experiment of Atmospheric Sciences. *China Meteorologcial Press*. 2002.

Tao, S., and L. Chen (1985), The East Asia summer monsoon. *Proceedings of International Conference on Monsoon in the Far East*, Meteorological Society of Japan, Tokyo, 1-11.

Tao, S., Y. Q. Ni, and S. X. Zhao, etc. 2001: The genesis, mechanism and prediction research of Chinese summer rainstorm in 1998. Beijing: Meteorological Press, 184pp.

Tao, S., Y. Zhao, and X. Chen (1958), The relationship between Mei-Yu in Far East and the behavior of circulation over Asia, *Acta Meteorological Sinica,* 29 (2), 59-74.

Tao, S.-Y., and Y.-H. Ding, 1981: Observational evidence of the influence of the Qinghai-Xizang (Tibet) Plateau on the occurrence of heavy rain and severe convective storms in China. *Wea Forecasting*, 2, 89-112.

Tao, S.-Y., Q.-Y. Zhang, and S.-L. Zhang, 1998: The great floods in the Changjiang River Basin in 1998. *Climatic Environ. Res.*, 3, 158-167.

THORPEX-China, *The Plan of the Observing System Research and Predictability Experiment-China* (in Chinese), Beijing, 2005, 25-26.

Tung, M. The impact of Tibetan Plateau on the environment evolution of western China. *Assessment of Environment Evolution of Western China.* Science Press (in Chinese), Beijing, China. 1, 147-170, (2002).

United Nations Environment Programme. Global Outlook for Ice and Snow Topographic maps. UNEP GRID-Arendal Library of graphics resources. http://www.unep.org/geo/ice_snow, 2007.

Wang, B., and Q. Ding, Changes in global monsoon precipitation over the past 56 years. *Geophys. Res. Lett.,* 33, L06711, doi:10.1029/2005GL025347, (2006).

Wang, J. Z, Ding, Y. H. Research on moist symmetric instability in a strong snowfall in North *China. Acta Meteor Sinica* (in Chinese), 1995, 53 (4): 451-459.

Wang, J. Z, Yang, Y., Modern Weather Engineering, Beijing, China *Meteorology Press,* 2000, 468pp.

Wang, J.-Z., Y.-Q. Yang, X.-D. Xu, and G.-Z. Zhang, 2003: A monitoring study of the 1998 rainstorm along the Yangtze River of China by using TIPEX data. *Adv. Atmos. Sci.,* 20, 425-436.

Wang, W, Cheng, L. S. Numerical study on three-dimensional conditionally symmetric instability of "96.1" snowstorm event. *Plateau Meteor.* (in Chinese), 2002, 21(3): 225-232.

Wang, W. H, Xu, X. D. The heavy snow process in district Xilingele and the analysis of "77.10" snowstorm. *Acta Meteor. Sinica* (in Chinese), 1979, 37(3): 80-86.

Wang, Y., L.R. Leung, J.L. McGregor, D.-K. Lee, W.-C. Wang, Y.-H. Ding, and F. Kimura: 2004: Regional climate modeling: Progress, challenges and prospects. *J. Meteor. Soc. Japan,* 82, 1599-1628.

Wang, Y., O.L. Sen, and B. Wang, 2003: A highly resolved regional climate model (IPRC–RegCM) and its simulation of the 1998 severe precipitation event over China. Part I: Model description and verification of simulation. *J. Climate,* 16, 1721-1738.

Wu, A., and Y. Ni, 1997: Numerical experiments of the influence of Qinghai-Xizang Plateau on the mean circulation of Asian monsoon. *Plateau Meteorology,* 16, 153-164.

Wu, G., 2004: Recent progress in the study of Qinghai-Xizhang plateau climate dynamics in China. *Quaternary sciences,* 24, 1-9.

Wu, G., Sun, L., Liu, H., et al. Impacts of sensible and latent heat flux over land surface on summer precipitation and subtropical high. Asian monsoon and Chinese torrential rain. Beijing, China *China Meteorological Press.* 1998a. 505pp.

Wu, G..-X., and Y.-S. Zhang, 1998: Tibetan Plateau forcing and the Asian Monsoon onset over South Asia and South China Sea. *Mon. Wea. Rev.,* 126, 913-927.

Xie, S.-P., H.-M. Xu, N.H. Saji, Y. Wang, and W.T. Liu, 2006: Role of narrow mountains in large-scale organization of Asian monsoon convection. *J. Climate,* 19, 3420-3429.

Xu X., L. Chen, and X. Wang (2004), Moisture transport source/ sink structure of the Meiyu rain belt along the Yangtze River basin. *Chinese Science Bulletin*, 49 (2), 181-188.

Xu, S. Y. The water vapor transportation and hydrological budget in China. *Acta Meteor Sinica* (in Chinese), 1958, 29(1), 33-43.

Xu, X., C. Lu, X. Shi, and S. Gao , 2008b: World water tower: An atmospheric perspective. *Geophys. Res. Lett.*, 35, L20815, doi:10.1029/2008GL035867.

Xu, X., M. Zhou, J. Chen, L. Bian, G. Zhang, H. Liu, S. Li, H. Zhang, Y. Zhao, D. Suolong, and J. Wang, A comprehensive physical pattern of land-air dynamics and thermal structure on the Qinghai-Xizang Plateau. *Sci. China (Series D)*, 45, 577-594, (2002).

Xu, X., Q. Miao, and J. Wang (2003), The water vapor transport model at the regional boundary during the Meiyu period. *Adv. Atmos. Sci.* 20 (3), 333-342.

Xu, X., C. Lu, X. Shi, and Y. Ding, The large-scale topography of China: A factor for seasonal march of the Meiyu-Baiu-Changma in East Asia. *J. Geophys. Res.*, 115, D02110, doi:10.1029JD012444, (2010).

Xu, X., R. Zhang, T. Koike, C. Lu, X. Shi, P. Li, S. Zhang, X. Cheng, L. Bian, and G. Ding, 2008a: A New Integrated Observational System over Tibetan Plateau (NIOST) for weather/climate monitoring and forecasting. *Bull. Amer. Meteor. Soc.*, 89, 1492-1496.

Xu, X.-D, M.-Y. Zhou, et al., 2001: Synthetic physical image of the dynamic and thermal structure of Tibetan Plateau land-air processes. *Science in China (D)*, 31, 429-440, (in Chinese).

Xu, X.-D., S.-Y. Tao, and J.-Z. Wang, 2002: The relationship between moisture transport features of Tibetan Plateau-monsoon "large triangle" affecting region and drought-flood abnormality of China. *Acta Meteor. Sinica*, 60, 257-266, (in Chinese).

Yanai, M., and C. Li, 1994: Mechanism of heating and the boundary layer over the Tibetan Plateau. *Mon. Wea. Rev.*, 122, 305–323.

Yanai, M., C.-Y. Li, and Z. Song, 1992: Seasonal heating of the Tibetan Plateau and its effects on the evolution of the Asian summer monsoon. *J. Meteor. Soc. Japan*, 70, 189-221.

Yanai, M., and R. H. Johnson, Impacts of cumulus convection on thermodynamic fields, *The Representation of Cumulus Convection in Numerical Models of the Atmosphere*, K.A. Emanuel and D.J. Raymond, eds., *AMS Monograph*, 24, 39-62, (1993).

Yanai, M., T. Tomita, Seasonal and Interannual Variability of Atmospheric Heat Sources and Moisture Sinks as Determined from NCEP–NCAR Reanalysis. *J. Climate*, 11, 463–482, (1998).

Yang, L., Miao, C. S, Shou, S. W. Numerical simulation on a snowstorm in Changjiang-Huaihe River Basin in spring 2003. *J. Nanjing Inst. Meteor* (in Chinese), 2006, 29 (3), 379-384.

Yasunari, T., A quasi-stationary appearance of 30 40 day period in the cloudiness during the summer monsoon over India. *J. Meteorological Soc. Japan*, 1980, 58, 225-279.

Yasunari, T., Kanehira, A, Koike, T. Seasonal and internal variability of snow cover over the Tibetan Platen and associated atmospheric circulation changes. *The Second Session of International Workshop on TIPEX2GAME/Tibet*, 2000, Kunming, China.

Ye, D. Z, 1981: Some characteristics of the summer circulation over the Qinghai-Xizang (Tibet) Plateau and its neighborhood. *Bull. Amer. Meteor. Soc.*, 62, 14–19.

Ye, D. Z, and Gu, Z.. On the influence of the Qinghai-Xizang Plateau on East Asian circulation and weather in China, *Scientia Sinica* (in Chinese), 1955, 4(1): 29-33.

Ye, D. Z., and Y. Gao, 1979: *The Meteorology of the Qinghai-Xizang* (Tibet) Plateau (in Chinese). Science Press, 278.

Yeh, T.-C., and Z.-C. Gu, 1955: On the influence of the Qinghai-Xizang Plateau on East Asian circulation and weather in China. *Scientia Sinica*, 4, 29-33, (in Chinese).

Young, G . S., Turbulence structure of the convective boundary layer. Part I: Variability of normalized turbulence statistics, *J. Atmos. Sci.*, 1988, 45(4): 719-726.

Young, G . S., Turbulence structure of the convective boundary layer. Part II: Phonenix 78 aircraft observations of thermals and their environment, *J. Atmos. Sci.*, 1988, 45(4): 727-735.

Young, G . S., Turbulence structure of the convective boundary layer, Part III: the vertical velocity budgets of thermals and their environment, *J. Atmos. Sci.*, 1988, 45(4): 2039-2050.

Yu, R., B. Wang, and T. Zhou, Tropospheric cooling and summer monsoon weakening trend over East Asia. *Geophys. Res. Lett.*, 31, L22212,doi:10.1029/2004GL021270, (2004).

Zhang Q., and S. Tao (1998), Tropical and subtropical monsoon over East Asia and its influence on the rainfall over eastern China in summer, *Quarterly Journal of Applied Meteorology*, 9 (s1), 17-22.

Zhang, Q., J. Lu, L. Yang, J. Wei, and J. Peng, The interdecadal variation of precipitation pattern over China during summer and its relationship with the atmospheric internal dynamic processes and external forcing factors. *Chinese J. Atoms. Sci.,* 31, 1290-1299, (2007).

Zhang, J. J., Zhu, B. Z. The Advance in Tibetan Plateau Meteorology (in Chinese), Beijing, China. *Science Press,* 1988, 268pp.

Zhang, R. The role of Indian summer monsoon water vapor transportation on the summer rainfall anomalies in the northern part of China during the El Niño mature phase (in Chinese). *Plateau Meteor,* 1999, 18(4): 567-574.

Zhang, X. L, Chen, L. S. Dynamic diagnose of the genesis and development for mesoscale shear line during "96.1" snowstorm I: Diagnoses of vorticity and vorticity variability. *Plateau Meteor* (in Chinese), 2000, 19 (3): 285-294.

Zhang, Z., H. Wang, Z. Guo, and D. Jiang. 2006: Impact of topography and land-sea distribution on EastAsian Poleoenvironmental patterns. *Advance in Atmospheric Sciences,* 23, 258-266.

Zhao, P, Chen, L. X. Climatic features of atmospheric heat source/sink over the Qinghai-Xizang Plateau in 35 years and its relation to rainfall in China. *Sci. China Ser. D-Earth Sci.,* 2001, 44(9): 859-864.

Zhou, M. Y, Xu X. D, et al. Observational Analysis and Dynamic Study of Atmospheric Boundary Layer on the Tibetan Plateau, Beijing, China. *Meteorological Press,* 2000, 125pp.

Zhou, T., L. Zhang, and H. Li, Changes in global land monsoon area and total rainfall accumulation over the last half century. *Geophys. Res. Lett.,* 35, L16707, doi:10.1029/2008GL034881, (2008).

Zhu, A. M, Shou, S. W. Diagnosis of frontgenetical secondary circulation in a winter snowstorm event. *J. Nanjing Inst. Meteor* (in Chinese), 1994, 17 (2): 183-187.

Zhu, B., 1990: The impact of the Tibetan Plateau on China's climate. The Blue book of Chinese Science and Technology. 5, *Climate.* China Science and Technology Publisher, Beijing, p320-324.

Zhu, Q., and J. Hu, 1993: Numerical experiments on the influences of the Qinghai-Xizang Plateau's topography on the summer general circulation and the Asian summer monsoon. *J. Nanjing Institute of Meteorology,* 16, 120-129.

Zhu, X., J. He, and Z. Wu, 2007: Meridional seesaw-like distribution of the Meiyu rainfall over the Changjiang-huahe River basin and characteristics in the anomalous climate years. *Chinese Sci. Bull.,* 52, doi: 10.1007/s11434-007-0280-3.

Zou, X, Xiao, Q. Studies on the initialization and simulation of a mature hurricane using a variational bogus data assimilation scheme. *J. Atmos. Sci.*, 1999, 57, 836-860.

INDEX